MICROSCOPY HANDBOOKS 13

An Introduction to Photomicrography

CW00739672

D. J. Thomson
Health and Safety Executive, London

Savile Bradbury
Department of Human Anatomy, University of Oxford

Oxford University Press · Royal Microscopical Society · 1987

Oxford University Press, Walton Street, Oxford OX2 6DP

Oxford New York Toronto
Delhi Bombay Calcutta Madras Karachi
Petaling Jaya Singapore Hong Kong Tokyo
Nairobi Dar es Salaam Cape Town
Melbourne Auckland

and associated companies in
Beirut Berlin Ibadan Nicosia

Oxford is a trade mark of Oxford University Press

Royal Microscopical Society,
37/38 St. Clements,
Oxford OX4 1AJ

Published in the United States
by Oxford University Press, New York

British Library Cataloguing in Publication Data

Thomson, D.J.
An introduction to photomicrography.
(Microscopy handbooks; 13)
1. Photomicrography
I. Title II. Bradbury, Savile III. Royal
Microscopical Society IV. Series
778.3'1   QH251
ISBN 0-19-856414-7

Library of Congress Cataloging Publication Data
Thomson, D.J.
An introduction to photomicrography.
(Miscroscopy handbooks; 13)
Includes index.
1. Photomicrography. II. Bradbury, Savile. II. Title.
III. Series.
QH251.T44 1987   578'.4   86-33220
ISBN 0-19-856414-7 (U.S. : pbk.)

Set by Grestun Graphics
Abingdon, Oxon
Printed in Great Britain by
The Alden Press, Oxford

Preface

Photomicrography is essentially a practical subject which cannot be mastered fully from books; only 'hands-on' experience can provide the ability to produce good photomicrographs easily and routinely. In a short monograph such as this, it is obviously only possible to outline some of the more important considerations, both on the microscopical and photographic side. We make no apology for perhaps over-simplifying and including (especially on the photographic side) descriptions of what may seem elementary and obvious to the more experienced micrographer. This was done for the benefit of those microscopists who are not photographers but would, nevertheless, wish to process their own photomicrographs. *Note*: Trade-names are printed in initial capitals; the mention of any such does not imply a recommendation or endorsement by the Royal Microscopical Society or the authors.

Acknowledgements

We wish to express our sincere thanks to our colleagues who have helped us by their helpful criticisms, especially Drs B. Bracegirdle and P.J. Evennett, together with the General Editor of the series, Dr C. Hammond.

London   D.J.T.
Oxford   S.B.
May, 1986

Contents

Introduction

Most users of the microscope need to record their observations for publication. Although many features of a microscopical image can be described in words, it is obvious that the inclusion of an illustration greatly increases the value of any report. Much time and effort is spent on achieving the best possible microscopical image, but often the results are presented by means of photomicrographs which do not do full justice to the quality of the microscopy. It is the purpose of this handbook to help all users of the microscope produce better micrographs to illustrate their work.

Since the earliest days of microscopy the need for illustrating microscopical observations has been apparent. Until the latter part of the nineteenth century, however, the technology available for this purpose was severely limited. Microscopists produced free-hand drawings which were then engraved onto wood-blocks or onto copper sheets. In the early nineteenth century lithographic techniques superseded copper-plate engraving for the illustration of papers on microscopy and this became the method of choice. With the pioneering work of Fox Talbot, Wedgwood and, in America (at a slightly later date) of J.J. Woodward the new process of photography was applied to the recording of images produced by the microscope. For many years **photomicrography**, as the new technique became known, was little used; the techniques were not easy and photographic emulsions of the time required long exposures. This did not, however, deter the enthusiasts, and during the 1880s many articles on photomicrography can be found in the *British Journal of Photography*, in the *English Mechanic* and in the *Amateur Photographer*. One such (published in the *British Journal of Photography* dated 5 October, 1883) described a horizontal photomicrographic camera which accepted plates six inches square and had a maximum extension of between 3 to 4 feet! Despite such experimentation, free-hand drawings made with the aid of a **camera lucida** and reproduced by lithography, remained the preferred methods of illustration for many years to come. With the increased availability of photographic plates of increased speed and of extended spectral sensitivity, and with the subsequent introduction of roll and cut-films, this situation began to change. By the early 1930s photomicrography was coming into its own. After the Second World War, the use of photomicrography was given an increased stimulus by the introduction of 35-mm colour film which was reasonably fast. This allowed the rapid production of transparencies for projection to illustrate lectures and soon this format became almost universal, not only for transparency work, but also for the production of black and white prints for the illustration of books and scientific papers.

Drawing the microscopical image has some advantages over photomicrography. Drawing allows the investigator to eliminate unnecessary detail from the image and so concentrate the observer's attention on relevant points. The production of a free-hand drawing not only requires accurate and correct observation and interpretation of the microscopical image, but also allows the microscopist to synthesize into one picture the results of a detailed examination of an object. This might be needed to allow the incorporation of detail which either lies in differing focal planes or which is learned from the examination of several microscopical fields or from different specimens. In addition, a drawing may be reproduced from a **line block**, which is cheap, when compared to a screened **half-tone block** required to reproduce continuous tones.

Drawings from the microscope may be produced free-hand if the microscopist is a skilled artist; usually, however, some form of accessory is required to allow the correct proportions to be established on the drawing. Such an accessory may be a camera lucida which is mounted above the eyepiece. This uses a small beam-splitting prism and a mirror to allow the microscope image and the drawing paper (which is placed at the side of the microscope) to be seen at the same time. The major features of the microscope image are then outlined, leaving the details to be added later free-hand. The modern version of the camera lucida is the drawing tube. This is mounted in the microscope body, above the nose-piece and below the binocular head. It acts in exactly the same way as the camera lucida and projects a real image of the sheet of drawing paper and the pencil into the primary image plane. The size of the visible field in the drawing plane can usually be altered by intermediate lenses in the body of the drawing tube so that drawings may be made to a given scale. These drawing tubes are now often used in conjunction with a digitizer pad as an aid to microscopical image analysis.

Against the above advantages of a drawing as compared to a photomicrograph, are the disadvantages that a drawing requires considerable technical skill to produce and it is always possible that bias, conscious or unconscious, could be introduced by the observer. At present, photomicrographs form the great majority of microscopical illustrations and therefore the ability to produce clear micrographs is an essential accomplishment for the microscopist.

Before any photography is undertaken with the microscope, care must be taken to obtain the very best possible microscopical image. Detail must be clearly resolved, with adequate contrast and presented in the image at a suitable degree of magnification. It cannot be over-emphasized that the image to be recorded on the film must be of the best possible quality. Many photomicrographs published in the journals are clearly taken using poor microscopical technique. It is not possible in this handbook to give detailed instructions in the correct operation of the microscope. Care is especially needed in the adjustment of the illumination system, especially in the correct setting of the illuminated-field and aperture diaphragms. Full details will be found in textbooks of microscopy or in earlier handbooks in this series. See for instance *An introduction to the optical microscope* by S. Bradbury, RMS Handbook No. 01 (1984).

The essential requirements of a photomicrographic system may be summarized as follows:

(1) It must produce a real image of the specimen (with minimal optical aberrations) in the film plane.

(2) There must be some means of knowing which area of the image is contained within the film format.

(3) There must be some means of indicating when the image is in sharp focus in the film plane.

(4) There must be some device for measuring the brightness of the image. This device may either indicate the required exposure time or control automatically the duration of the exposure.

(5) There must be some form of shutter to interrupt the light beam and allow the film to be exposed for the requisite time.

Some of these requirements will now be considered in more detail.

1.1. Microscope–camera systems

The compound microscope produces a virtual final image of the specimen, i.e. it cannot be projected onto a screen; ideally, this image is located at infinity and the rays of light emerging from the eyepiece will be parallel.

In a photomicrographic camera system the final image must be real, and located in the film plane at a finite distance from the eyepiece. If the microscope is simply refocused in order to achieve this (i.e. the specimen–objective distance is altered) then image quality (especially with an objective of high numerical aperture) will be poor. This is because such re-focusing introduces considerable spherical aberration into the image. Two methods are used to produce a real image on the film without destroying the optical corrections of the system:

(1) A **projection eyepiece** is used in the microscope tube; this lens looks superficially like a normal eyepiece but produces a real image at a fixed distance from its top lens whilst maintaining the optical corrections of the system. No other lens is used between the projection lens and the film plane (Fig. 1A).

(2) A **normal eyepiece**, designed for visual observation, is used in the microscope tube together with a camera system containing a converging lens (or system of lenses) arranged to form a real image on the film from the parallel light leaving the eyepiece. Again, this prevents the introduction of spherical aberration into the final image as the microscope does not then need significant re-focusing in order to produce this real image at a finite distance from the microscope eyepiece (Fig. 1B).

Both systems allow the user to alter the total magnification of the real image by changing the projection lens or the eyepiece, in exactly the same way as the image magnification may be changed for visual work by substituting a different eyepiece. It is essential that the correct type of eyepeice or lens be used in a photomicrographic system. A system designed to use a projection eyepiece will not work

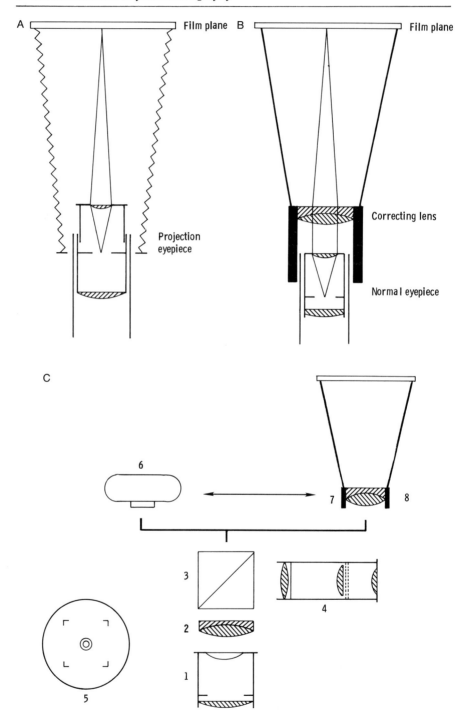

Fig 1. (A) A diagram to illustrate the formation of a real image on to a film by means of a projection eyepiece, here shown in a camera fitted with a bellows. The projection eyepiece differs from an ordinary eyepiece in that the distance between its lenses is variable so as to produce an aberration-free image at varying distances from its top lens when the camera extension (and hence the image magnification) is changed.

(B) A diagram to illustrate the formation of a real image by means of a normal eyepiece used in conjunction with a convex lens fitted into the camera body to prevent the introduction of aberrations consequent upon forming a real image at a finite distance above the eyepiece. The distance between the lens and the film plane is fixed and is arranged either for a large-format image, e.g. 5×4 inch or for the 25×36-mm image of the 35-mm film format. The magnification thus cannot be changed by varying the camera extension.

(C) A diagram to show the components of a photomicrographic system which is adaptable to give either 35-mm or large format pictures. (1) Normal eyepiece fitted in the microscope tube. (2) Lens for use with the 35-mm body to give an aberration-free image at a finite distance from the eyepiece. (3) Beam-splitting prism. (4) Focusing telescope with graticule to frame the image field. (5) The image of the frame as seen in the telescope. The lines delimit the image which will be received by the film; the lines forming the double circle must be sharply focused at the same time as the image in the telescope in order to ensure sharp focus on the film plane. (6) 35-mm camera back interchangeable with (7). (7) Large format back. (8) An extra lens fitted in the large format back to compensate for the increased extension.

correctly with a normal eyepiece in the microscope tube; conversely, a photomicrographic system corrected for use with a normal microscope eyepiece will give poor results if a projection eyepiece is used. It may also be wise to avoid using optics of differing manufacture in the same system — an eyepiece which gives good results in its original instrument may perform less well in another piece of equipment from a different maker.

There is much variety of equipment for photomicrography currently available, accepting different film sizes and of varying degrees of complexity. Perhaps the most widely used instrument is fitted with a trinocular head; inclined binocular viewing eyepieces are provided for observation together with a third vertical tube on which the camera system is mounted. There may be a beam-splitting arrangement in the camera tube with a small focusing telescope (Fig. 1C); alternatively, a framing eyepiece may be fitted in one of the binocular viewing tubes. This provides a frame, visible at the same time as the image, showing the area recorded at the film plane. The system is so arranged that the image is sharp on the film if it is in focus at the same time as the framing graticule is in sharp focus. A range of camera bodies is provided to enable the film size and format to be changed as necessary.

Some makers now supply large photomicrographic systems in which the photographic equipment is integrated into the body of the microscope, using a specially-designed projection lens system, often of great complexity! Such equipment is usually provided with automatic exposure and motorized film-winding facilities. Current models are, for example, the 'Polyvar' from Reichert, the 'Axiophot' from Zeiss (Oberkochen), the 'Vanox' from Olympus, and the 'Microphot' from Nikon.

1.2. Viewing and focusing systems

The simplest of these, common in large-format cameras, is a ground glass screen, mounted in its own holder which is inserted into the film plane. When the shutter is opened, the image may be observed directly and focused with an accessory magnifier. Often a small area of the glass screen is left clear to make focusing easier at low light levels.

With the introduction of 35-mm cameras, the separate ground-glass screen became impractical. An optical system is therefore used to view and focus the image (Fig. 1C). Such systems vary widely between different makers in their details but all are similar in principle. A beam-splitter (consisting of a cube made up of two 45° prisms cemented together on their hypotenuse) fitted in the camera head diverts some of the light from the microscope into a telescope which faces the operator. This telescope has a focusing eyepiece and contains a graticule showing the film format frame. In addition to the frame, the graticule usually has some aid to critical focusing, often in the form of two finely engraved concentric circles or a set of double lines in the form of a cross. The graticule is placed in the telescope barrel in a plane which is accurately parfocal with the film plane of the camera.

Before use, the telescope eyepiece must first be focused on the graticule with no specimen in the field of view. The adjustment is correct when, with the eye relaxed, the cross lines of the graticule are clearly seen as being double. The specimen may then be brought into the field; it will be in focus at the film plane when both it and the double cross lines are seen in sharp focus at the same time. An accessory magnifier is sometimes fitted to the front of the telescope to give an enlarged image of the centre of the field of view. This is a great help in attaining sharp focus when using the lowest powers or if the user has a tendency to accommodate whilst using the microscope.

As mentioned above, many modern instruments do not use a beam-splitter in the trinocular head but arrange for the image to be framed by a graticule fitted into one of the observation eyepieces. The graticule is so arranged that when it is in focus at the same time as the microscope image the latter will also be sharply focused in the film plane of the camera.

1.3. Exposure determination

The determination of the correct exposure is perhaps the source of most difficulties in photomicrography. Most modern camera systems avoid many of the difficulties by incorporating some form of photoelectric sensor in the beam-splitter of the viewing system. The signal from this sensor is then used to indicate the required exposure, or now more commonly, to control electronically the camera shutter so that the correct exposure is automatically given when the release button is pressed. In this case, the user may have no indication of the duration of the exposure being given, but some of the more elaborate instruments display the intended exposure and indicate throughout its duration the passage of elapsed time.

Automatic exposure systems work very well for much of the time, especially when the image is homogeneous and occupies most of the film frame. Often, however, the user does not know just how much of the image area is being used for the determination of the exposure. If the whole area of the frame is used for an integrated measurement of brightness, then specimens viewed by dark-ground illumination or by fluorescence (where small bright features are seen against a black background), will give rise to grossly over-exposed pictures. This is because the integrated measurement by the sensor registers a low overall image brightness. This problem can be overcome by using a 'spot' measurement. Here only a small part of the image, usually the central area defined by the circle in the centre of the framing graticule, is measured. Any small, bright feature measured in this way will be correctly exposed, as will others in the same field of view, whilst the background will register as a true black. Such instruments in which there is selection of full frame or spot measurement as required are available only at the upper end of the price range. With cheaper instruments it is often possible for the user to determine for himself the size of the measurement area by moving a single bright particle across the field of view and observing the output of the exposure meter. Alternatively, if no meter is provided, the variation of exposure given by the automatic camera unit is noted when the particle is at the centre of the field and then at varying distances from the centre. A centre-spot metering system will give very much shorter exposures when the particle is in the centre of the field than when it is at the edge. A full-field metering system will give exposures which vary only slightly with the position of the particle in the field.

It is important to realize that even with fully automatic camera units it is not sufficient just to set the instrument to the nominal speed of the film. It is advisable to calibrate the unit for the film–developer combination in use by making a series of exposures on a typical specimen, varying the film speed setting for each exposure. When this test strip is developed it will then be possible to assess the most suitable speed setting for one's own particular application. The spectral response of the sensors is not uniform over the whole of the visible spectrum, so if deep red or blue filters are to be used, it is necessary to make a further series of test exposures with the filter in place. Examination of these negatives will then allow the selection of a suitable setting for that particular film–filter–developer combination on the instrument.

The provision of automated exposure measurement in a system is usually coupled with a motorized film advance. This not only simplifies usage but prevents unintentional double exposures and blank frames on the film.

Although most modern systems are provided with automatic exposure measurement, on occasion older equipment has to be used. It is then important to assess correctly the required exposure. There are several possible ways in which this may be done. If working with a 35-mm camera mounted on a microscope fitted with a trinocular head, a commercial photoelectric exposure meter (such as the 'Lunasix' or the 'Profisix', both produced by Gossen, the Minolta 'Auto meter' III or IIIF fitted with the booster attachment, or the 'Microsix' which was formerly available from Leitz) may be used. These are fitted with a special probe which replaces one of the eyepieces of the microscope. The film speed is set on the exposure meter, the probe inserted in place of one of the eyepieces and a reading of the light intensity taken. In conventional photography, the required exposure for the f-aperture in use on the camera would then be read off from the calculator dial of the meter. As the microscope camera system is not calibrated in this fashion, some form of index on the meter is used instead of the f-aperture setting. The correct index for the film–developer combination in use must be determined by taking a light reading, and then exposing a trial strip of film, varying the exposure through a wide range. When this test strip is developed the correct exposure time may be found by inspection of the negatives; it is then easy to correlate this with the correct index setting on the meter.

In the above method the light intensity remains constant and the exposure time is varied. It is also possible to operate in the converse way and determine the correct light intensity for a given exposure, say 1/10 sec or 1 sec. This has the disadvantage that if a rheostat is used to vary the intensity of the light, its colour temperature will fall as the intensity is lowered. With black and whilte film this does not matter, but with colour film such a procedure will cause unacceptable changes in the colour rendering. It is possible to take colour micrographs and adjust the exposure in this manner if the light intensity is reduced by means of neutral density filters and *not* by lowering the lamp operating voltage.

For the highest quality micrographs, a large-format camera using 4 X 5 inch sheet film is needed. This may consist of an adaptor which fits onto an automatic system in place of the 35 mm back, when all the automatic exposure metering facilities will still be available. If, however, the system is a simple bellows camera fitted onto an ordinary microscope, then no such facility will be available. In this case the exposure is measured with a sensitive photoelectric meter directly on the ground glass of the camera back, taking care to exclude ambient light from the measuring probe. Calibration is done by trial and error, often using a stepped exposure on a single sheet of film, in order to find the correct setting for the index on the meter. Exposure determination is simplified if a 'Sinarsix' film-plane meter is available. This meter consists of a cassette which carries a movable probe bearing a photoelectric sensor linked by a cable to the measuring meter. The cassette displaces the ground glass to allow the probe to be moved about in the actual film plane in order to measure the light intensity at known points in the image. By the use of this sophisticated and expensive equipment, precise exposure measurements are obtained, a matter of importance when shooting with large format colour film!

Although some components are basic and are found in all available microscope camera systems, there are many variations in matters of detail. The correct use of instruments from different makers and of various degrees of sophistication can only be ascertained by a careful reading of the instruction manual. A good general motto would, therefore, be

When in doubt – READ THE MANUAL!

Two of the frequent sources of difficulty when using unfamiliar equipment should, however, be briefly mentioned at this point. The first is that there may be no image in the viewing telescope whereas there is a perfectly good image visible through the normal binocular head. This signifies that there is a control knob or lever (operated by the user) which diverts the light from the viewing to the photographic system and vice versa. In the absence of precise instructions, a little careful observation should find the relevant control (which often does not bear any indication of its function). Open the unloaded camera back and look down into the shutter unit. Press the camera shutter button on the control unit; if the control lever is incorrectly set no light will be seen as the shutter opens. Repeat the process after operating any likely control until light is seen as the shutter opens. The second problem arises from the fact that most camera bodies are provided with some form of shutter or dark slide to enable the user to remove the camera and so change from one format to another in the middle of a roll of film. In the case of 35-mm camera bodies this device is likely to be small, black, and inconspicuous! Check carefully on your system whether such a safety slide is present and if so, make sure that it is withdrawn from the light path before taking pictures. Overlooking the safety slide causes many feet of unexposed 35-mm film to be processed annually! Some manufacturers interlock the safety slide with the shutter so that the latter will not operate until the slide is in the correct position. This certainly saves film but if the user is unaware of the interlock such a mechanism may well result in a needless call to the service engineer.

1.4. Photomicrography with miniature cameras designed for normal photography

Most standard 35-mm camera systems include a *microscope adapter* in their range of accessories. This is a metal tube fitted with some form of clamp which allows it to be attached firmly to the microscope tube. In use, the microscope eyepiece is retained and a real image is formed in the film plane by altering the focus of the microscope; the reflex viewfinder of the camera is used to determine the correct focus. If the microscope adapter is a plain, empty tube, then producing a real image at a finite distance from the exit pupil of the microscope by re-focusing may introduce noticeable spherical aberration into the image. This is especially apparent with high-aperture dry lenses. Some improvement may be obtained by raising the microscope eyepiece from its normal position by means of a small collar. The thickness of the collar should be such that no re-focusing is needed when changing from visual observation *without* the collar to observation through the camera viewfinder *with* the collar in place on the eyepiece. This thickness is most easily found by experiment. Some of the more expensive microscope adapters, however, contain an accessory lens designed to avoid the need of re-focusing the objective and with these an eyepiece collar is not required.

These simple microscope–camera adapters use the camera's focal plane shutter with the camera mirror being automatically raised out of the light path. This may cause mechanical vibrations and consequent loss of sharpness of the image, especially at high magnifications. Contrary to one's initial thoughts, the effects of vibrations due to this can be reduced by using a *longer* exposure time, so that the vibration has ceased for most of the exposure. Similarly, trouble may be caused with these microscope–camera adapters by drifting of the focus during the period of the exposure. This may be troublesome during long exposures and if the focus mechanism of the microscope acts on the limb of the instrument rather than on the stage. Many users of this type of micrographic camera find it difficult to focus accurately as the grain of the camera viewfinder screen often obscures much of the fine detail in the image. Again, if the focusing screen is fitted with microprisms or a split-image rangefinder, difficulties may be experienced. These are not designed to operate with the small f-apertures found in microscopes and 'black out', so obscuring some of the image. If interchangeable screens are available than a plain ground glass, often with a clear centre spot, is best. Even with the finest screen possible it is not easy to focus accurately and a 'through focus' series of exposures is recommended if the use of such equipment cannot be avoided.

1.5. The use of bellows cameras

The **bellows camera** consits of a strong vertical pillar mounted on a stout base plate. The pillar carries on a movable arm a front plate which is usually fitted with the upper half of a light-trap attachment and a Compur-type shutter. This plate is mounted parallel to the base plate and is adjusted in height to lie just above the eyepiece of the microscope tube which is fitted with the lower half of the light trap. The lower camera plate is united by a bellows with a second movable plate which forms the camera back. This carries a ground-glass screen for focusing the image. Most micrographic cameras of this type will cater for 5 × 4 inch sheet film carried in standard dark slides, a 120 roll-film adapter or a 'Polaroid' instant film back. The use of a film size of 5 × 4 inch ensures the best quality and as exposures are processed individually, it is possible to exert the maximum amount of control. The principal disadvantages of this type of equipment are that operation is rather slow, most systems do not possess automatic metering and exposure facilities and the cost of the film is much greater than 35 mm. This is somewhat offset by the availability of a greater range of emulsion types.

   With such systems there is a choice between the use of a normal eyepiece fitted with a lifting collar (as described above), the use of a variable-focus projection eyepiece or the use of a normal eyepiece and increased microscope tubelength. Each of these will avoid the spherical aberration which would otherwise be introduced by altering the specimen-to-objective distance. When using a bellows camera the microscope does not support the extra weight of the camera, and the camera and microscope are usually separate. This means that exposures are less likely to suffer from loss of sharpness due to mechanical vibrations than when a miniature camera is in use, attached directly to the tube of the microscope.

   The use of any conventional camera tripod to support a camera in a position which is suitable for photomicrography is an exercise which should only be considered as a last resort. Even with a good quality professional tripod whose rigidity is not in question, achieving the accurate alignment of the camera–microscope system to a common optical axis is a procedure of great difficulty. If circumstances force you to attempt photomicrography in this way, it helps if the microscope can be placed on a very low table or other rigid support which is small enough to fit between the legs of the camera tripod. If you intend to use a vertical microscope tube, check that the tilt movement on the tripod has sufficient range of travel to permit the camera to be positioned with its optical axis pointing vertically downwards, as not all commercial pan-and-tilt heads will allow this.

2

Some basic photographic theory

The light-sensitive agent in a photographic system is a suspension of silver halide crystals (usually the chloride, but the bromide and iodide are also used) in a gelatin-based medium. This forms the **emulsion** which is coated onto glass plates or a flexible polyester film for use in a camera, or onto paper for the production of prints.

When light falls onto the crystals in a photographic emulsion some of them are affected by photons, so leading to the formation of active centres in those crystals which have been exposed. This exposure produces no visible effect but leaves a **latent image** on the film. The number of active centres per unit area of film is governed not only by the intensity of the light falling on the emulsion but also by the duration of the exposure. Crystals containing active centres will react with mild reducing agents in aqueous solution and are converted into grains of metallic silver; this process is called **development** and the image so produced is a **negative**, because the bright areas in the original scene are reproduced on the film as black metallic silver. The dark areas of the subject cause no exposure of the halide crystals; no active centres are formed in them and they are not therefore, affected by the developer. As this unchanged silver halide is still light-sensitive it must be removed in order to make the image permanent. This is performed by dissolving the unchanged silver halide with (for example) sodium thiosulphate, a process known as **fixation**.

The response of a photographic emulsion to light may be represented graphically by plotting the optical density of the silver in the negative against the logarithm of the relative exposure. This is done in practice by exposing successive frames of film in a camera to an evenly-lit white card. The lighting and lens aperture are kept constant for each exposure in the series but each successive exposure is twice as long as that preceding it. In this way a series of ten negatives may be obtained in which the exposure range is from 1024 to 1. If the optical density of each negative is measured with a transmission densitometer and the values then plotted against the logarithm of the relative exposure, a curve similar to those shown in Fig. 2 will be obtained. Such a curve is called the **characteristic curve** and represents the behaviour of that particular film for a given developer used for a stated time. It can be seen from (A) in Fig. 2 that the characteristic curve has a S-shape, with a 'toe' at low log-exposure levels followed by a 'straight-line' portion leading to a 'shoulder' at the higher levels of exposure where the curve is beginning to flatten out. The exposure should be such that the darkest shadow area of the subject in which detail is required should give a negative density which lies on the straight-line part of the curve just above the toe. If this is done then other shadow areas of luminance higher than the darkest shadow area in the subject will fall on the straight-line portion of the curve and thus have increased densities in the negative. This will enable the differences in shadow detail to be rendered satisfactorily in the print. If the negative is **under-exposed**, then the low levels of luminance in the various shadow areas of the subject may all fall on that part of the toe of the curve which is almost parallel to the baseline and will register on the negative as areas of similar density which it will not be possible to separate in a print. The density range of the negative has thus been compressed and shadow detail is being lost. Conversely, if the subject receives significant **over-exposure** then the highlight luminances will come to lie on the shoulder of the curve with a consequent inability to separate highlight details in a print. Fortunately, most subjects have a range of luminance which is less than that of the straight-line portion of the characteristic curve of the film so that by giving a suitable exposure the full range of the subject's luminance may be recorded on the film.

It will be seen that even when there is no exposure the optical density is never zero, but stays at a low value over a range of exposures. This represents what is called the **base plus fog density**, and is due to the small amount of metallic silver produced by the action of developer on unexposed silver halide grains, together with any density due to the film base itself. This base plus fog density is normally low, as may be seen at the edges of any negative where the film has passed over the film guides in the camera. A high base plus fog density indicates the presence of some defect in the system such as the use of old film, film which has been stored at too high a temperature, film which has been exposed to light, the use of an unsuitable developer, or too high a processing temperature.

The slope of the characteristic curve indicates the contrast of the negatives produced by the use of a particular emulsion – developer combination. This contrast range is the most important factor to be considered when choosing a film for any given purpose, as the manufacturers produce a range of emulsions having widely differing contrast ranges. A material intended for the copying of line drawings, for example, will produce a high contrast negative with no grey tones between the minimum and maximum densities. Such an emulsion will have a steeply rising characteristic curve (curve B in Fig. 2). A material designed for general studio-portrait photography, on the other hand, where a wide range of subject brightness must be faithfully reproduced, will require a characteristic curve with a much lower slope. This indicates that the emulsion is capable of reproducing a large number of intermediate grey tones between the maximum and minimum densities (curve A in Fig. 2). Comparison of the contrast of different films may be done by the use of a numerical parameter called the **contrast index** (introduced by Kodak) which is listed in the technical data provided by the maker of the emulsion. The contrast index is defined as the slope of the line joining a point on the characteristic curve where the image density exceeds the base fog level by 0.1 or 0.2 density units to a point on the curve at a density of 2 units above the lower level (Fig. 3). In the older literature, contrast of an emulsion is represented by the expression 'gamma' but this has largely been superseded by the concept of contrast index as defined above.

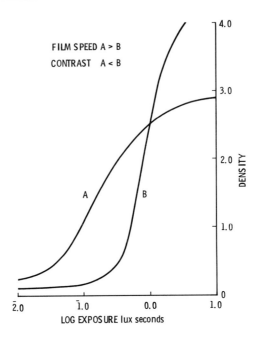

Fig. 2. The characteristic curves for two different films given the same development. Film A is for general-purpose use and has a medium contrast. Film B has a much steeper curve and with this development would give a high contrast negative with few grey tones. Film A would be faster than film B and would have more exposure latitude.

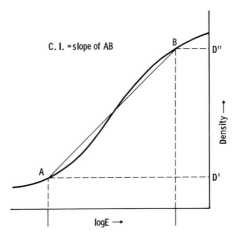

Fig. 3. The characteristic curve of a film to show how contrast index (C.I.) is defined. C.I. is the average value of the slope of the part of the curve between point A (0.2 density units above base fog) and point B which is 2.0 density units higher than A. The ordinate of the plot represents optical density whilst the abscissa represents the log (relative exposure). Curves redrawn from Kodak Data Sheet P255, with permission.

2.1. Contrast control

Although the **contrast** achieved in any given negative is chiefly dependent upon the type of emulsion used, the actual value of the **contrast index** produced by any given emulsion is also dependent on the type of development which it receives. This means that the contrast can to some extent be varied by the user. The factors which may be used to control the contrast of the negative are:

(1)   The formulation of the developer.
(2)   The development time.
(3)   The temperature of the developer.

Most manufacturers give details of the different developers which can be used with their films, and the values of the contrast index which result. In general, the fine-grain developers (such as 'Microphen' from Ilford, 'Microdol-X' from Kodak or 'Aculux' (FX-24) from Patterson) used for 35-mm materials produce low-contrast negatives whilst more energetic developers ('D19' or 'HC110' from Kodak, for example), give much higher contrast.

Contrast is greatly affected by the duration of development, increasing as the time is prolonged. For example, the contrast index of Kodak 'Plus-X' film developed in 'HC110' may be varied from 0.45 (with 3 min development) to a maximum value of 0.8 with development extended to 15 min. The increase of grain size and clumping with prolonged development is a factor which must be taken into account when using this technique with small film sizes. Slow-speed films are often used in photomicrography, where long exposures are acceptable. As such films usually have a fine-grain emulsion which produces a higher contrast than the faster films used in general photography, extended development is rarely needed in practice. If, however, it is employed then the intrinsically fine grain of the slow film ensures that the final graininess of the negative is not usually a problem, even when a 35-mm negative is enlarged to give a print 10 × 8 inch in size. Kodak 'Panatomic X' and Ilford 'Pan F' are two examples of slow speed fine-grain films that are available. For work requiring maximum contrast, a film such as Kodak 'Microfile AHU 5460' (designed for continuous tone copy work) is useful. It should be noted that 'Microfile' film, in common with many other technical types of emulsion, is only available in 100 feet rolls, so that 35-mm cassettes must be loaded by the user before such materials can be used in a normal camera. If an orthochromatic emulsion (see p. 17) is needed then the use of Agfa 'Ortho 25' should be considered.

Extended spectral sensitivity, together with a very fine grain and good contrast are all achieved by the use of Kodak 'Technical Pan' film (Type 2415). It is best processed in either 'HC110' or 'D19' developer, although other developers (e.g. Agfa 'Rodinal' diluted 1:50) may be used. Experiment will be necessary in order to determine the most suitable concentration, development time and film speed setting. With the recommended developers 'Technical Pan' may be rated at between ISO (ASA) 50 and 100, according to the development. A specially formulated developer for this film is Kodak 'Technidol LC'. This produces much lower contrast

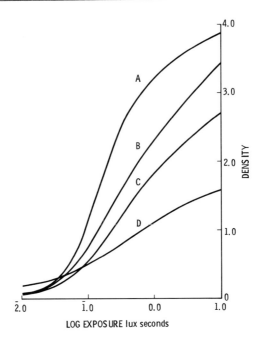

Fig. 4. Characteristic curves for one film (Kodak 'Technical Pan 2415') following different development procedures. (C.I. = Contrast Index). (A) Developed in 'D19', 4 min, C.I. = 2.4. (B) Developed in 'HC110' (1 + 9), 6 min, C.I. = 1.65. (C) Developed in 'HC110' (1 + 9), 4 min, C.I. = 1.25. (D) Developed in 'Technidol LC', 15 min, C.I. = 0.56.

negatives and is often recommended for pictorial work. When 'Technical Pan' is used with this developer, its speed falls to about ISO 25. The flexibility of this film is illustrated by its characteristic curves which are shown in Fig. 4. From this it may be seen that a wide range of negative contrasts is possible with this emulsion by using different developers. With 'Technidol LC' the contrast index is 0.56; by using 'HC110' for different times this figure may be increased from 1.25 to 1.65. If Kodak 'D19' is used as the developer, then the contrast index can reach 2.4. 'Technical Pan' is available in both 35-mm and 4 × 5 inch sheet film and is a highly recommended film for many branches of scientific and technical photography.

2.2. The spectral response of photographic emulsions

(A) *Panchromatic emulsions*

Most films for general use, in both 35-mm and roll-film formats, are **panchromatic emulsions**. This means that such films are sensitive to light of all wavelengths in the visible spectrum (Fig. 5). Any colour in the spectrum will be reproduced as a grey tone whose density depends on the subject brightness (Figs 6 and 7). Such a wide spectral response means that these materials must be processed in total darkness.

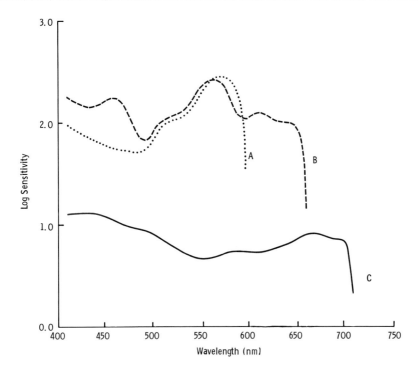

Fig. 5. The spectral response curves of orthochromatic, panchromatic, and extended-red sensitive emulsions (A, B, and C, respectively). The height of the curve at any point gives an indication of the relative sensitivity of the film at that wavelength.

Other emulsion types, having different spectral responses, are available for special purposes; for example the response in the red wavelengths may be extended (Fig. 5) in some films intended for scientific and technical use.

(B) *Orthochromatic emulsions*

Orthochromatic emulsions are insensitive to the longer, red, wavelengths of the spectrum (Fig. 5) and may be processed in red light. Negatives made with such emulsions produce prints in which red areas appear dark, whilst blue and green features are reproduced correctly (Fig. 6). This property may sometimes be used to great effect to enhance the contrast of small red features in a mainly blue or green specimen. Orthochromatic materials are most readily available in sheet film, but Agfa 'Ortho 25' is available in both 35-mm and 120 roll-film format.

(C) *Blue-sensitive (ordinary) emulsions*

Blue-sensitive emulsion types are those with which the first photographs were taken. They are sensitive only to the blue and ultra-violet end of the spectrum with a response which falls off rapidly above about 520 nm. The use of these materials for normal photography or photomicrography produces results which appear bizarre! For example, oranges photographed on such a film appear in the final print as black lustrous cannon balls, whilst blue objects show exaggerated brightness. Such a blue-sensitive emulsion (for example, Kodak 'Fine-grain Positive film') is widely available in 35 mm and is much used for producing positive black & white transparencies intended for projection. This emulsion can be used as a negative emulsion for photomicrography if the user is aware of the possible false colour renditions which may arise. Blue-sensitive and orthochromatic emulsions are much

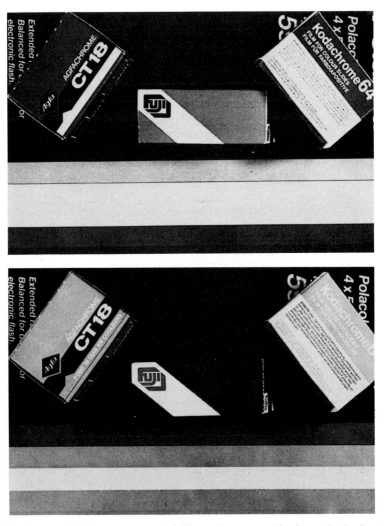

Fig. 6. A photograph of some commercial film packages on orthochromatic (*top*) and panchromatic emulsions (*bottom*). Note that in the orthochromatic emulsion, the reds in the picture appear very dark by comparison with their appearance in the picture made on panchromatic film. Compare with the colour photograph (Plate 1A) which shows the same objects.

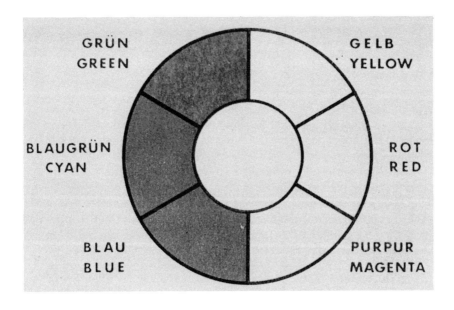

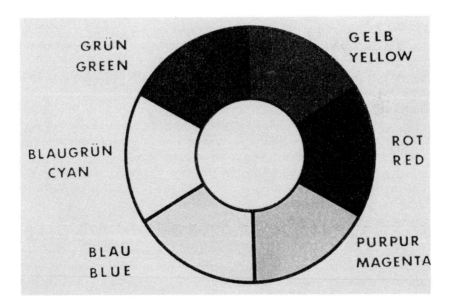

Fig. 7. The colour circle (See Plate 1B) photographed on panchromatic film through a deep-red filter (*top*) and a deep-blue filter (*bottom*). In the image recorded in red light, note how the yellow, red, and magenta segments appear light in tone, whereas in the blue-light image it is the cyan, blue, and (to some extent) the magenta segments which are light in tone. In the colour circle itself, note that complementary colours lie diametrically opposite to each other.

used in metallography, where the specimens often show little colour. For such use the resulting fine-grain, high-contrast negative with its very low base fog level, is advantageous.

(D) *Infra-red films*

Materials with special sensitization to make them responsive to the long wavelengths of infra-red radiation have been used in many scientific applications of photography, although their use in photomicrography is limited. **Infra-red films** have a basic panchromatic response with the red sensitivity extended to ca. 900 nm. This type of film is exposed with a very deep red (often visually opaque) filter in the system; this removes the visible light to which the film is excessively sensitive. Because the image produced by the camera or microscope lens at a wavelength of 900 nm is in a different focal plane from that produced in the visible regions of the spectrum, a focusing correction must be made if the pictures taken in infra-red are to be sharp. One good method (taken from the Kodak publication *Applied Infra-red Photography*, No. M28, 1977) for making this correction is as follows:

(1)   Focus the image visually, with a 'Wratten 61' green filter in the light path.
(2)   Note the reading (say 8 units) of the fine focus knob of the microscope against its index.
(3)   Re-focus the image with a 'Wratten 29' red filter in place of the green.
(4)   Note the new fine focus reading (say 13 units).

The required empirical additional focus correction which must be applied to achieve sharpness in the infra-red may be obtained by taking the difference between the red and green readings ($13 - 8 = 5$ units in the example given above) and multiplying by 2 if an apochromat lens is in use (or by 1.4 for an achromat). In our example, assuming an apochromat is in use, this would give an index increment of 10 units, so the final setting on the fine adjustment would be $13 + 10 = 23$ units. In order to eliminate any possible backlash in the fine focus mechanism of the microscope, the focus shift should always be effected in the same direction (from green to red) as the index numbers are obtained or are reset.

Infra-red materials are rather sensitive to light and temperature, so it is important to comply exactly with the manufacturer's instructions regarding their handling, processing and storage.

2.3. Film speed

Two films may differ markedly in the exposure which they require to produce negatives of a similar density from the same subject under identical lighting conditions. The film requiring the lesser exposure is said to have the higher speed, which thus varies inversely with the exposure required. Many other factors (e.g. colour of the exposing light, whether we are working at extremes of light intensity, composition and time of action of the developing agent) are also involved in the expression of the speed of an emulsion. To compare the speed of different films, and to enable the required exposure to be measured, various index number systems have been introduced. The two systems in common use at the present are the **ASA (American Standards Association)** and **DIN (Deutsche Industrie Norm)** standards, although the ISO recommendations are now superseding the former in many countries. In practice, the **ISO (International Organization for Standardization)** number may be taken as equal to the ASA speed index. It is not possible here to enter into the theoretical or practical details of how such numbers are derived; full details are available in the textbooks of photographic theory listed in the bibliography. In both systems a high number indicates a film of high speed. Conversely, a low value of the ISO or DIN number indicates that the film has a low speed and hence will need either a high light intensity or a long exposure time to produce a negative which is correctly exposed.

The DIN system is logarithmic, and is so designed that a speed number increase of three units represents an increase in film speed by a factor of two. In other words, a film rated at DIN 27, for example, will be twice as fast (and hence require half the exposure) as a film rated at DIN 24. The ISO and ASA systems, on the other hand, are arithmetic and the film speed or sensitivity is directly proportional to the ISO number. In this system a film having an ISO speed rating of 100 requires only half the exposure needed by one rated at ISO 50 or twice the exposure for a film rated at ISO 200, assuming the light level remains constant. A comparison between ISO and DIN speeds is given in Table 1.

Table 1. *Comparison of International Organization for Standardization (ISO) and Deutsche Industrie Norm (DIN) film speeds*

ISO	DIN
6	9
8	10
10	11
12	12
16	13
20	14
25	15
32	16
40	17
50	18
64	19
80	20
100	21
125	22
160	23
200	24
250	25
320	26
400	27
500	28
650	29
800	30
1600	33
3200	36

The correct speed number for any material is quoted in the manufacturer's literature and printed on the package. It is important to remember that the figure given applies only to the film when certain specified processing conditions are employed. The use of a developer other than that specified may well require the use of a revised ISO or DIN speed number, which would have to be determined by experiment. Some developers have been specially formulated to increase the film speed and these represent an extreme example of this principle. By the use of such developers a film nominally rated at ISO 400, for example, may be uprated to ISO 1600 with only slight loss of quality. This technique is not commonly used in photomicrography with black and white film stock, but it can also be applied to the first development of a colour film. This may be of use when fluorescence micrographs have to be produced on reversal film. It should be remembered also that the maker's film-speed recommendations are devised for use in conventional photography. It is quite possible that there may be wide variations in the calibrations of various types of photomicrographic equipment; this means that the speed quoted should be regarded only as a guide. It is essential when using any equipment for the first time, or when using a new type of film or developer, to expose a test strip, varying the film-speed setting on the instrument through a range of values. When this has been processed it is possible to judge the best setting for the particular conditions in use. When using colour transparency film it is often advantageous to uprate the film speed by 50 per cent in order to obtain a greater saturation of the colours. The ISO or DIN speed ratings should only be used as a guide – in photomicrography conditions are so variable that an empirical approach is often the only one to adopt.

2.3. Reciprocity failure

The ISO or DIN film speed will be found to be approximately correct (with the reservations mentioned above) in many of the situations normally encountered. The film-speed values, however, do not apply in situations where high levels of image brightness require extremely short exposures or where the brightness is so low that the exposure needs to be very long. Under either of these conditions films will be found to be less sensitive than their quoted speed numbers imply. This effect is called **reciprocity failure**; it means that at the extremes of image brightness, more exposure time is required than indicated by the measured light intensity.

In photomicrography the most common cause of reciprocity failure is due to long exposure times. For example, when using methods such as phase-contrast or fluorescence or when examining specimens of low reflectivity by reflected light, there is likely to be an image of low brightness and the indicated exposure time of many seconds would fall into the range at which the film shows reciprocity failure. Some photomicrographic camera systems now feature exposure-control circuitry in which the response is made non-linear, giving added exposure time when the light level is low. In many instruments such a compensation is fixed by the maker but in many of the more versatile photomicroscopes there is a variable control by means of which the user can select the appropriate degree of correction depending on the film in use. If photomicrographs taken at low brightness levels consistently appear to be under-exposed then reciprocity failure should be suspected. The user may alter the specific control, if fitted, or make the system give longer exposures by setting the film-speed control to an empirically-determined lower value. If future pictures are taken at approximately the same image brightness with this new speed setting, then correctly exposed negatives or transparencies should be obtained routinely. Reciprocity failure may also occur when flash photomicrography is carried out with dedicated systems as the exposures tend to be very short. With black and white films there is sometimes a problem when the exposure is increased to compensate for reciprocity failure. In these cases the highlights are over-exposed when the detail is rendered correctly in the darker areas. This may be corrected by reducing the development time for film exposed under such conditions or by using a compensating developer (see a textbook of photography for details of these). With colour transparency films, in which there are three emulsion layers, each sensitive to a different colour, there is the possibility that reciprocity failure may occur in one or more of the emulsion layers and not in the others. This results in a colour cast in the final reversal transparency. It is possible, however, to compensate for these if exposures are likely to be prolonged by adding a colour compensating filter to the light path; details of the colour and correct strength of such filters must be determined by experiment.

3

Some techniques in photomicrography

3.1. The use of colour filters

Colour filters are used in black and white photomicrography for two main reasons: first to improve the optical resolution of the microscope objective and secondly to control the contrast in the image. Most microscope objectives suffer to a greater or lesser degree from residual spherical and chromatic aberrations. With high-quality lenses these may not be of great significance, but if photographs have to be made with objectives of mediocre quality, then a great improvement may often be obtained by taking monochrome photographs with a narrow-cut green filter. This restricts the wavelength of the image-forming light to a narrow band around 550 nm, a region at which most lenses give their best performance. If the specimens are not themselves coloured, then it is a good practice to take all black and white photographs in green light.

The use of colour filters to modify contrast or tonal range with panchromatic film is much more important. This is often needed when stained sections containing more than one colour have to be reproduced. Without a filter, areas of the specimen of the same brightness reproduce as areas of a similar grey tone, even though to the eye they are of different colour. The resulting print will thus be lacking in contrast between areas of, say, red and blue, assuming that they are of the same brightness. The choice of which filter to use is generally simple, and is based on the rule that a feature in the specimen will be darkened in the print if a filter of the complementary colour is used. The relationships of the primary colours and their complementaries may be illustrated graphically by the so-called **colour circle** (Fig. 7 and Plate 1B) in which any colour is diametrically opposite to its complementary colour. From this it will be seen that a blue feature will be darkened by a yellow filter, magenta-stained material will be darkened by a green filter and green features darkened by a red filter. Conversely, coloured objects will be rendered light in tone if they are photographed on panchromatic film through a filter of the *same* colour (Fig. 7). The use of a colour filter to darken any given colour also makes small differences in the intensity of that colour more apparent and hence improves the contrast even when only that colour is present in the specimen.

Colour filters are commercially available in various grades, in both glass and in stained gelatin. These latter are obviously cheaper, but are much more liable to damage by scratching and mechanical handling. It is possible for the microscopist to produce some colour filters very cheaply by using conventional biological stains on unexposed, fixed photographic film. Full details of the dyes and method will be found in an article by Bradbury (1985), listed in the bibliography.

Table 2. *Filters for black and white photomicrography selected from the Kodak 'Wratten' series*

'Wratten' No.	Colour	Effect
11	Light yellow	Darkens blue
15	Deep yellow	
22	Deep orange	
25	Red	Darkens green
29	Deep red	
35	Deep magenta	
45	Blue–green	Darkens red
47B	Deep blue	Darkens orange–yellow
58	Green	Improves definition with achromatic objectives

A useful range of filters for black and white photomicrography is the 'Wratten' series by Kodak; Table 2 represents a useful selection.

In order to achieve the desired contrast, the filters sometimes need to be quite dense so that the increase in exposure time required can become very great. This may pose problems with mechanical vibrations if the shutter is open for long periods and hence every effort must be made to try and ensure that any microscope-camera system has adequate mechanical rigidity. Another problem in the use of colour filters is that the spectral response of the exposure measuring system may not match the sensitivity of the film when the wavelength range of the illumination is restricted by the use of dense colour filters. This can only be resolved by making test exposures at various film-speed settings when an unusual filter combination is used for the first time. An alternative procedure is to measure the exposure without the filter and then *increase* the reading by a known value (the **filter factor**) which is determined from the literature or by an empirical trial. Such adjustments are most likely to be required when deep-blue or deep-red filters are in use.

It should be remembered that the resolution of the microscope is dependent (among other things) on the wavelength of the illuminating light. The best resolution is obtained with blue light, whilst resolution is poorest in red. This means that if dense-red filters are required to produce a useful contrast then some loss of resolving power is inevitable; this is made worse by the poorly corrected spherical aberration of achromatic objectives at these long wavelengths. The use of an apochromatic objective will produce the best results under these conditions.

Filters are most conveniently placed in the illuminating system of the microscope; this means that they do not need to be of such high optical quality as filters placed in the imaging system or on a camera lens. As mentioned above, gelatin filters may be used provided that they are placed in a suitable location in the microscope system. On occasion, even the plastic coloured gels used for stage lighting may be used as contrast filters for microscopy, although it must be remembered that they may pass a wide range of wavelengths and hence their suitability for any application must be tested empirically. The holder below the substage condenser is one common location for filters, but in many microscopes this position is very close to the plane of the aperture diaphragm, which in Köhler illumination receives an image of the lamp filament and thus may be a point at which considerable heating can occur. If the filter is a cheap gelatin type then it may be easily replaced if damaged by over-heating, but expensive glass-mounted gelatin filters or polarizers are best placed elsewhere. A point midway between the field diaphragm and the substage condenser is ideal, if such a place is conveniently accessible in the system. If placed *too* close to the field diaphragm, the surface of the filter will be imaged in the same plane as the specimen and scratches, dust or other imperfections will be in focus with the image.

In order to avoid heat from the lamp damaging any filters, it may be possible to fit a heat-absorbing glass into the system. Many makers fit such a glass as standard and if this is so it should be apparent from the instruction manual. If no heat absorber is fitted and it is not possible to fit one, then any colour filter should only be left in place for the period of the actual exposure and removed afterwards. Interference filters and filters made from glass dyed in the mass are not usually susceptible to damage by heat.

3.2. Processing black and white films

Many books and articles have been written on this subject, some of which are listed in the bibliography. It is proposed to give only a very brief account here in order to introduce the basic principles involved, with sufficient practical details to enable the worker with no photographic experience get started.

All handling of panchromatic film until it has been fixed must take place in darkness. With roll film in the 120 size there is no need for a fully-equipped dark-room, as the film stock is purchased in a form ready to load into the camera: 35-mm film is usually purchased already loaded into cassettes in either 36 or 20 ex-posure lengths, although it is often cheaper and more convenient to load one's own cassettes from bulk film. Such a length (often about 100 feet) may be loaded in a darkroom into a so-called **bulk-loader** which will then allow any desired length to be loaded into cassettes without further need of a darkroom. If sheet film is in use, then a darkroom is essential to load the film holders. It is now possible to ob-tain so-called **instant print** materials which do not require any dark room for their processing (see Chapter 6).

After exposure of the film it must be developed and fixed to produce a perma-nent image. This process is usually done in a **developing tank**. Some of these, for both roll film and 35-mm film formats, are of the so-called **daylight-loading** type and they allow the whole of the negative processing to take place in the light. Most tanks, however, require the film to be loaded in the dark into a plastic or metal spool which has spiral grooves in its upper and lower plates to hold the film and prevent adjacent turns touching each other. If this happens then incomplete development and fixation will result in spoiled areas on the film. When the film is loaded into the spiral, it is important not to touch the emulsion with the fingers. If this does happen, then the contamination from sweat and other substances on the fingers may lead to fingerprints appearing on the negative. Some spirals have some form of ratchet mechanism to enable the film to be loaded by a gentle back-and-forth twisting movement of the plates. Other types (especially professional ones made of stainless steel) may require a special loading guide to be used, although with practice the film may be loaded correctly by feel alone. *The use of force to persuade a reluctant film to enter the spiral must be avoided*, as the mechanical stresses so induced produce active centres in the emulsion which develop as black streaks on the negative.

The loading of a developing tank with panchromatic film MUST be done in TOTAL darkness and this operation requires a certain degree of skill and confidence. This can rapidly be acquired by practice with some scrap film in the light. If no darkroom is available, a changing bag can be used or the operation can be carried out inside a large cupboard; many rolls of film have been developed without difficulty using the wardrobe in an hotel bedroom as an improvised darkroom for the loading of the tank! The spiral into which the film is loaded must be absolutely dry, as the slightest trace of moisture will cause the film to stick. Once the film is safely in the spiral, the latter is placed in the tank and the lid screwed on. All the remaining operations can then be carried out in the light because solutions can be poured into and out of the tank through light traps built into the lid of the tank.

Details of the many types of developer, temperature, dilution, and the time for which they are allowed to act are all to be found in the literature provided by the film manufacturer or in photographic reference books. The instructions should be followed carefully, at least until familiarity in the use of any particular film–developer combination has been achieved. During development it is desirable to agitate at intervals so as to ensure that the developer is thoroughly mixed and by-products of development do not accumulate close to the film, where they may affect its development. Agitation is sometimes carried out by rotating the spiral in the tank, but more commonly the whole tank has a tight-fitting lid and is simply inverted to mix the contents. The agitation process should be standardized as far as possible (say, three inversions every minute). When development is complete the developer is followed by a **stop bath** of 2 per cent acetic acid for about 1–2 min before fixing for about 2 min in one of the commercial rapid-fixative solutions. After use, both stop bath and fixer may be returned to their stock bottles and re-used many times; most developers are used once only and then discarded. The final stage in processing a monochrome film is to wash it well with running water for about 30 min. This is usually done with the film still in the spiral, but of course, the lid of the tank may be removed for this process. It is as well to resist the temptation to withdraw the film for examination, as the emulsion is still soft and may easily be damaged mechanically at this stage. After washing give a final rinse in distilled water to which a little photographic wetting agent has been added. This will ensure that the film will dry evenly and without any drop-like marks on the emulsion (due usually to hardness in the water). Drying the film is carried out by unrolling the film carefully from the spiral, fixing a clip to each end and suspending it in a dust-free place to dry naturally. Alternatively, films may be dried rapidly in a cabinet through which heated air is circulated. These work well, but if old and rusty, or if their air intake is near floor level they should be regarded with suspicion as they may then draw dust into the cabinet and deposit it in an even layer all over the film!

With sheet films, processing may be carried out by unloading the film in the dark and clipping it to a special hangar which supports it through the development, stop bath, fix, and wash stages. The solutions may be in shallow dishes or, more often, in large vertical tanks.

Processing of black and white films is a relatively simple operation and should not give rise to many problems. Some possible difficulties, however, may arise from any wide departures from the recommended temperature. This should be normally $20°C$ and most formulations of developer quote the time of development for this temperature. The extreme limits for normal processing should be regarded as from 15 to $25°C$, with suitable adjustment of the time. Special developer formulae are available for use in tropical extremes of climate. Another difficulty may arise from the exhaustion of developer. This problem is more likely to arise when sheet film is processed in tanks holding 20 litres or more of developer. When such tanks are used it is necessary to keep a record of the number of sheets of film which have been processed so that allowance may be made for the exhaustion. It is possible to obtain replenisher kits, but as developer is relatively cheap (as compared to the time of the photomicrographer!) it is generally better to dispose of partially exhausted developer and replace it with fresh solution. If working with 120 roll film or with 35-mm film which is developed in a tank holding a small quantity of solution then it is far better to use fresh developer for each film. *Never return partially used developer to a stock bottle for further use.*

Another problem which may arise is that oxidation of the stock or partially diluted developer solutions may occur in the bottles. This may cause unusual effects if such solutions are used to develop films. This may be avoided by storing developers in the plastic concertina bottles which are now readily available and squeezing them to expel all the air contained above the level of the liquid. If these are not obtainable, then the level of the liquid may be raised by dropping small glass marbles into the stock bottle or with some developers (such as the Kodak 'HC110') by *not* making an intermediate dilution — as Kodak recommends — but leaving the concentrate in the bottle and diluting this directly just before use to the actual working concentration. The concentrated syrup is much less likely to be degraded by oxidation than the partly diluted intermediate working solution. If this technique is used, however, it is essential to have the means of measuring accurately small amounts (of the order of 10 ml or less) of the rather viscous developer concentrate.

3.3. Printing black and white negatives

A **print** is the positive image formed on photographic paper by light which has passed through the negative, so that the density distribution of silver in the print is the inverse of that in the negative.

The emulsion of a black and white printing paper is blue-sensitive, so that exposure and all the subsequent processing may be carried out in the darkroom under an orange or yellow safelight. All 35-mm negatives must generally be enlarged with a high-quality lens which projects an image of the negative down onto the printing paper on the baseboard of the enlarger. Even illumination of the negative is essential and this is most commonly achieved by the use of a **condenser lens system** mounted immediately above the negative, between it and the lamphouse. For 35-mm negatives, an enlarging lens of about 50 mm focal length would be used, whereas for the larger formats the enlarging lens would have a focal length of 105 or even 150 mm. The enlarger lens is always fitted with an iris diaphragm which allows the lens aperture to be varied. In practice the lens is only used at its maximum aperture for focusing the image and then it is closed ('stopped down') for the actual exposure. This ensures that the optical performance of the lens is optimum and prevents very short exposure times.

There are two main problems in producing a good print. One is the choice of a satisfactory grade of contrast for the printing paper and the other is the determination of the correct exposure. Printing paper conventionally comes in five or six different grades of contrast, ranging from 0 to number 5. Grade 0 or grade 1 is very 'soft' and if a normal negative, correctly exposed and with an average range of contrast, is printed on it the resulting print would have a very limited range of contrast with many shades of grey and no true blacks (Fig. 8A). A similar negative printed on grade 4 or 5 paper would give a 'hard' print, with deep blacks, clear whites and few tones of grey (Fig. 8b). The best results from a correctly exposed, correctly developed negative with an extended tonal range covering both white, greys and black would be obtained by printing on a 'normal' paper of grade 2. Experience alone can teach the correct grade of paper to use with any given negative. Formerly it was desirable to keep a stock of each of the grades of paper in order to cope with the odd negative. Now, however, some manufacturers produce paper with variable contrast which may be controlled by varying the colour of the exposing light by means of filters. This is a very convenient system and has much to commend it.

Printing paper formerly consisted of a high-quality paper coated with the photographic emulsion. Such a paper was absorbent and soaked up the chemicals used to process it, and therefore needed careful washing to remove the absorbed chemicals before it was dried. Although the traditional paper is still obtainable, most scientific photography would be done on RC or resin-coated paper. This consists of a thin layer of paper sandwiched between two plastic coatings so that only the photographic emulsion absorbs any of the processing chemicals. This means that the washing time is reduced and there is no need for the traditional glazing on a highly polished heated sheet of metal in order to produce a glossy print. RC paper may be simply allowed to dry naturally or it may be rapidly dried in a hot-air dryer if many prints are being produced. RC paper is available with many surface textures but traditionally photomicrographs for scientific use are produced on glossy-surfaced paper.

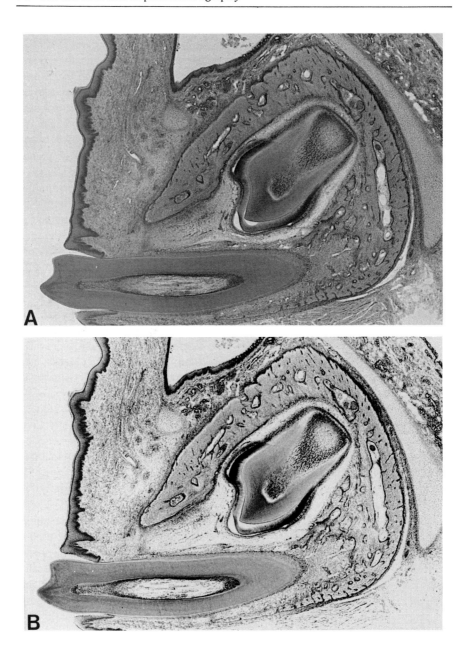

Fig. 8. A low-power photomicrograph of the incisor tooth of a kitten; the negative, which was of normal contrast, is printed here for comparison on very 'soft' paper (grade 0) and on very 'hard' paper (grade 5). With 'soft' paper (A) the image is mainly in grey tones with no true black, whereas with a very 'hard' paper (B) the image is extremely 'contrasty' and is largely expressed in blacks and whites.

Although **photoelectric enlarging exposure meters** are now available, the determination of the correct exposure is still most simply and reliably done by producing a graded series of exposures. To do this, a sheet of paper is positioned in the masking frame and the whole exposed for 1 sec. A narrow strip of the paper on one side is covered with card and a further exposure of 1 is given. The card is then moved along, covering up more of the paper, and another exposure of 2 sec given. Successive movements of the card and further exposures of 4, 8, and 16 sec may then be made. When a print produced in this way is developed it will show strips of gradually increasing density so that the time of exposure needed to produce the most satisfactory density may be judged (Fig. 9). A further slight adjustment to the exposure may be needed to produce a print of the highest possible quality, but with

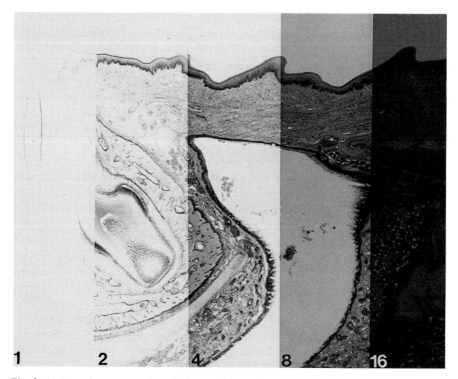

Fig. 9. A stepped-exposure print which would be made to serve as a test for the determination of the correct exposure during enlargement. The figures indicate the exposure (in seconds) which each step received.

experience such adjustments may be assessed without difficulty. If a great deal of printing is done, a photoelectric exposure meter may well repay its cost in time saved and by preventing wastage of printing paper. Such meters have to be calibrated, but once this has been done and if they are used with common sense, they are very valuable darkroom accessories.

In many cases, if the micrographic negative has been correctly exposed and the microscope illumination properly adjusted, a straight print will be perfectly acceptable. Occasionally, however, some feature may record with too much density on the negative, so that on printing it appears as an area of white, lacking in detail when the print exposure is correct for the remainder of the field. This may be remedied during printing by giving the dense area more exposure than the remainder of the print, a process often called **burning-in**. The background exposure is made in the normal way; this is followed by switching on the enlarger light again whilst at the same time shading the correctly exposed parts of the print with either a sheet of card or the hands. If a small area only is to be given more exposure then a hole in a sheet of card makes a suitable mask. Conversely, part of the print may require a little less exposure than the surrounding field. Such **shading** or **dodging** is done with a small circle or elliptical shape of card fixed onto the end of a wire handle which allows the area to be protected from the light whilst the remainder of the print receives the extra exposure needed. Any form of dodging or shading requires the mask to be kept in constant motion during the time of the additional exposure in order to avoid a hard shadow effect on the print; *it must be stressed that some practice and skill is needed to achieve satisfactory results*. The aim should be to produce negatives which, as far as possible, do not require special attention during the printing process.

The developer and fixing solutions used for papers are not the same as are used in film processing. Paper developers need to be more active than most film developers in order to produce good black tones and many are specially formulated to minimize the risk of staining of the paper during the processing which normally takes place in an open dish under suitable safelighting. The fixer solution used for papers is normally the same as that used for film but it is used at a greater dilution; full directions are always provided by the makers of the chemicals. It might perhaps be stressed here that *paper must be developed fully in order to obtain good blacks and a correct range of contrast*. A print which has been over-exposed in the enlarger **cannot** be saved by shortening the development time in order to maintain a correct optical density; such a **'pulled' print** will appear muddy and lacking in contrast. The only remedy is to expose another sheet of paper correctly and give the full development time as recommended by the manufacturer. Similarly, an under-exposed print cannot be saved by prolonging the development time much beyond that recommended. Prints left in developer for an excessive time usually become stained and unusable. It is desirable to pass the developed prints rapidly through a wash bath of either clean water or a stop bath consisting of 1 per cent acetic acid before placing them in the fixer. This has the advantage that development is quickly stopped and that the fixing solution is not contaminated with developer. It is always desirable to handle the paper in the developing and fixing dishes with some form of plastic print tongs. This ensures that the operator's hands do not become contaminated with chemicals (which might be transferred to the next sheet of paper) and prevents any risk of the solutions affecting the skin and causing a contact dermatitis.

Photomicrography in colour

It is possible in a short monograph to give only the most elementary principles of colour photography, together with a few practical details so that the microscopist may begin to produce transparencies for illustrating his work. Those who wish for more detailed information should consult some, or all, of the sources listed in the bibliography.

4.1. Additive and subtractive colours

Any colour may be reproduced by the mixing or addition, in correct proportions, of light of the three primary colours — red, green, and blue. If suitable intensities of these colours are present, white light results, whereas if only two of the primaries are added then a secondary colour is produced. Red and blue add together to produce magenta, red and green give yellow, whilst green and blue produce cyan. This is termed **additive colour mixing**. If a colour television picture is examined with a 10X hand lens, it will be seen to be composed of a regular array of fine dots. These are dots of phosphor which when excited by the electron beam glow either red, green, or blue; all the colour information in the picture is transmitted in terms of the relative intensities of these colours. If an area which appears pure yellow on a TV screen is examined, it will be found that only the red and green phosphor dots are activated — no blue dots will be seen.

If coloured paints, dyes, or inks are mixed then we have the converse situation, termed **subtractive colour mixing**. This may be illustrated by placing coloured filters in front of a source of white light. If a fully saturated red filter is used, then it will transmit only red light, and will absorb blue and green. Similarly, a green filter will transmit green and absorb red and blue whilst a blue filter will transmit blue and absorb red and green. Combining filters of any two of these primary colours will result in no light passing at all whilst combining filters of any *two* of the secondary colours yellow, magenta, and cyan will result in light of the primary colour which is a common constituent of the two secondaries. Thus yellow and cyan together pass green, cyan and magenta pass blue and magenta and yellow pass red. If filters of all three secondary colours are combined in front of a source of white light, no light will pass as there is no colour which is common to all three. Exactly the same applies to light reflected from coloured paints or inks on white paper. Most colour reproduction processes and colour films rely on the subtractive colour mixing, using only dyes of the three secondary colours — magenta, yellow, and cyan — to reproduce the colours of the original.

Photographic films similarly resolve the colour in the original subject into three primary components not in the form of a dot matrix but in the form of three superimposed images. This is achieved by coating the film with three separate emulsion layers, one above the other, each one sensitized to a primary colour and producing its own complementary colour dye image in an amount corresponding to the amount of colour present in the object. All three layers are affected simultaneously and in the subsequent processing a negative silver image is first formed in each layer; after the dye image has been created, the silver image is removed leaving the dye images which recreate the original colour by subtractive colour mixing.

4.2. Colour negative films

When the final result is to be a colour print, in general photography it is usual to use **colour negative film** in the camera. This film has three emulsion layers sensitive to the three primary colours as described above and it is designed to produce an image in which not only are the tones reversed, as in monochrome negatives, but also the colours, each being represented in the negative as its complementary colour. A bright-yellow object, therefore, will produce a dark-blue image whilst a red object will reproduce as pale blue–green. The coloured dye image is produced in the film in the first stage of development, along with the silver image; after fixation to remove unexposed halides, the silver image is bleached away, leaving just the negative dye image in its complementary colours. These colours are not obvious on an immediate inspection of the negative, as they are superimposed upon an orange background. This is due to another dye (the **integral colour mask**) which is built into the film by the manufacturer and is intended to improve the reproduction of the colours in the printing stage.

The colour negative is printed onto a colour print paper using conventional photographic techniques to give a final image with the correct colours and tones. The advantage of the colour negative/print system lies in the ability of the photographer to control the density and the colour balance of the final print. This is done by varying the exposure and by the use of colour filters in the enlarger during the printing exposure. The darkroom facilities for the printing of colour negative films should be more sophisticated than for standard monochrome photography. Precise control of the temperature of the processing solutions and of the timing of the various steps is essential, together with the use of a stabilized power supply for the enlarger lamp so that its colour temperature remains constant. The enlarger should also allow for correct colour filtration; this may be in the form of gelatin filters placed in a drawer inserted into the light path. In more sophisticated systems, the colour of the light is varied by means of dichromatic filter wedges moved into the light path by dials calibrated in terms of the units used to specify the colour printing filters. Such **colour heads** as they are called, are a great convenience if much colour printing is undertaken. As colour printing paper is sensitive to infra-red radiation, a barrier filter for these long wavelengths of radiation should be permanently inserted into the light path of the enlarger. Such a filter will also act as a heat filter.

If colour negative material is to be used for photomicrography without 'in-house' print processing facilities being available, the results are liable to be very disappointing if the printing is entrusted to the average retail store which provides amateur film-processing services. This is because colour printing for the amateur market is carried out on fully automatic machines. When a negative is put into such a device its colour distribution is measured by a colour analyser and filters are introduced to the machine. Such a system works well with holiday snaps of people and places, but negatives having a preponderance of one colour (say, crystals viewed between crossed polarizers with a first-order red plate added) will be detected by the colour analyser as having excess magenta. The printing machine will, therefore, compensate for this by adding excessive green to the print. The only satisfactory solution to this problem is to use a commercial processing firm who produce high-quality hand-printed work for professional photographers and to provide them with precise written instructions describing the desired result. Even better, send them a good colour transparency and ask them to match the print to that.

4.3. Colour reversal films

Colour reversal film materials are used to produce positive colour transparencies directly on the original film, ready for viewing by projection or, in the case of large format images, directly on a light box. Reversal materials generally produce better colour than all but the very best colour prints made from colour negative and as their processing is relatively simple (provided that accurate timing and temperature controls are adhered to) they can be handled in any moderately well-equipped darkroom. The only item of equipment which might not normally be available is a constant-temperature water bath which is used to maintain the solutions at the correct temperature before and during the processing. It is, however, true to say that unless much colour processing is undertaken, it is not economical as the chemicals do not keep well once they have been made up into working solutions. Most colour transparency films are returned to the manufacturer for processing but there are many professional colour laboratories who will undertake this service. This guarantees the quality and consistency of the processing. The disadvantage of all reversal transparency systems is the inability to alter the final result after the film has been processed. Density, colour balance, and saturation must be correct and this can only be achieved at the exposure stage. It is possible to obtain duplicate transparencies from colour slides made on reversal film and colour prints are also possible, either via an intermediate colour negative or by the use of reversal colour printing systems. Only the high cost of materials tends to prevent a much greater use of colour prints in scientific posters and for theses.

Paper and chemicals for making colour prints are available in small quantities and the technique is not very difficult. The exposed paper is usually processed in a tank similar to that used for film development, agitated by rotation on a set of motorised rollers, so that the changing of solutions may be done in the light. Perhaps the most widely used technique is the Ilford 'Cibachrome' process. This works on the dye–bleach principle in which dyes incorporated in a three-layered emulsion are removed during the processing to leave the correct amounts of yellow, cyan, and magenta to produce correct colour rendition in the final image. 'Cibachrome' is easy to process, as there are only four steps (development, bleaching, fixing, and washing) in the production of a finished print. 'Cibachrome' prints show a high colour saturation, excellent sharpness, and have a considerable resistance to fading in the light. Recent changes in the composition of the paper, together with the use of the correct chemistry have resulted in a wide-exposure latitude and colour balance latitude.

Another widely-used process is the Kodak 'Ektaflex' system which is an example of a dye-transfer process. A sheet of film is exposed in the enlarger in the usual way, as if it were conventional printing paper, before it is treated with a single activator solution. The wet film is rolled, by means of a small manually-operated machine, onto a sheet of 'Ektaflex PCT' paper. The film and the paper are left in contact for a time, during which the dye image transfers from the film onto the paper. After a short time the colour print is separated from the film and left to dry. Two types of 'Ektaflex' material are available, one for use with transparencies, the other for the printing of colour negatives.

4.4. Colour temperature

Colour films can only correctly reproduce the original colours when the subject is illuminated at the time of the exposure by a light source having the spectral energy distribution for which the film is designed. It is a matter of common experience that the light from a candle flame is more yellow than that from an electric light bulb, which in its turn, is more yellow than daylight. If the temperature of the tungsten filament of an electric lamp is progressively increased by increasing the current passing through it from an initial low value, then the colour of the light emitted changes as the temperature changes. At a low filament temperature, the light is reddish, whilst at high temperatures the light contains more of the shorter, blue wavelengths and so appears whiter. The ratio of blue to red in the spectrum of the light emitted by a hot body increases therefore as the temperature increases. Using this principle, it is possible to specify the colour quality of a light source by means of a number known as the **colour temperature**. This value (which may be measured by simple photoelectric meters) is expressed in units called Kelvins, K. The approximate colour temperature of various light sources is listed in Table 3.

While it would be possible to make a colour film which is balanced for any colour temperature, in practice only three types are produced which suffice or almost all applications. These are:

> Daylight film Type S —   balanced for 5500 K.
> Artificial light film Type A — balanced for 3400 K.
> Artificial light film Type B — balanced for 3200 K.

The two different artificial light films are produced because over-run professional studio lamps generally operate to produce light at 3400 K whilst other types of

Table 3. *Colour temperature of light sources*

Light source	Colour temperature (in Kelvins, K)
Wax candle	1930
6V, 30W microscope lamp run at 6V	2700
Gas-filled tungsten lamp	2700–2900
6V, 30W microscope lamp run at 9V	3200
12V, 100W QI lamp	3250
Photoflood lamp	3400
Carbon arc	3800
Noon sunlight	5400
Average daylight	5500–6500
Electronic flash tube	6000
Blue sky	12 000–18 000

studio lighting equipment in common use operate at 3200 K. The photographer obviously selects the appropriate type of film for the lighting units in use, although with the increasing use of electronic flash and of QI lighting units in professional studio work it is possible that Type A film will soon become unavailable. Colour temperature matching of the light source to the type of film in use, applies to both colour negative and colour reversal films. The manufacturer's literature should be consulted to ascertain the correct colour temperature for which any particular colour film is balanced.

The colour temperature of any light source may also be expressed in MIREDs, an acronym derived from the term *MI*cro *RE*ciprocal *D*egrees. The mired value is given by the relationship:

$$\text{MIRED value} = \frac{1\ 000\ 000}{\text{colour temperature (K)}}$$

The relationship between MIREDs and Kelvins is shown diagrammatically in Fig. 10.

Jenny and Panozzo-Heilbronner (1981, a,b) have written on the colour temperature of light sources likely to be met with in microscopy and in macrography. They consider low-voltage lamps, both conventional as well as tungsten–halogen and provide data for colour temperature both when the lamps are operated at the normal voltage and when they are 'over-run'. This latter greatly increases the colour temperature but only at the expense of dramatically shortening the life of the lamp. In the same articles, they also consider ring sources with fluorescent tubes and suggest possible filtration to achieve satisfactory colour rendering with such sources.

It frequently happens that the colour temperature of the light source used in a microscope does not match the required value for the film in use. Micrographs taken under such conditions will have a marked colour cast. Daylight colour film exposed in a microscope using a light source with a colour temperature of, say, 3250 K will provide pictures which appear with the reds strongly emphasized. This may be appreciated by comparing Plate 2A, exposed with light of too low a

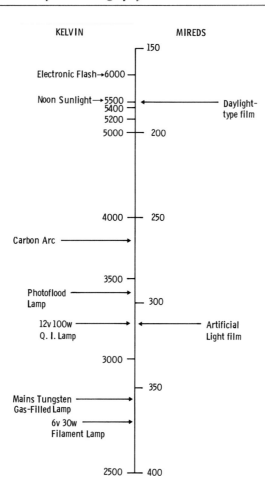

Fig. 10. A diagram to illustrate the relationship between colour temperature expressed as MIREDs and as degrees Kelvin.

colour temperature, with Plate 2B which was exposed at the correct colour temperature. In extreme cases this phenomenon may result in images with an overall reddish or orange cast. If artificial light colour film is exposed by means of electronic flash then the converse effect will result and there will be a strong blue tint to the micrographs. If micrographs have to be taken with a mismatch between the colour temperature of the light source and that for which the film is corrected, then the perceived colour temperature of the light source must be changed; this can most easily be done by means of a colour-balancing filter placed in the light path of the microscope.

In order to assist in the calculation and selection of the correct filtration to use, a value called the 'MIRED shift' is used. This indicates by how much (in MIREDs) the filter will alter the colour temperature of the light which it transmits. An **increase** in the colour temperature of the light passed (i.e. the light becomes more bluish) gives a negative MIRED shift, whilst an orange or yellowish filter will result in a lowering of the colour temperature and gives a positive MIRED shift. The MIRED shift of any given filter as quoted by the manufacturer is constant, whatever the colour temperature of the light source, although the **absolute** value of the change in colour temperature will, of course, depend on actual colour temperature of the light source in use. In practice, the MIRED value for the colour temperature (CT) of both the lamp and the film must be calculated from the expression given above. If the two values are different then a filter whose MIRED shift is such that:

MIRED value of lamp + MIRED shift due to filter = MIRED value of film

must be placed in the light path. The calculations involved may be illustrated by two examples.

Example 1

CT of light source   = 3200 K (= 313 MIREDs)
CT of film balanced for daylight = 5500 K (= 182 MIREDs).

The required filtration is given by the relationship:

MIRED shift of the filter (S) + CT of lamp (in MIREDs) = CT for which film is balanced.

By substitution we get
$$S + 263 = 313,$$
therefore
$$S = 182 - 313$$
$$= -131 \text{ MIREDs}$$

The filter required must have a MIRED shift of −131, which approximates to a 'Wratten 80A'.

Example 2

CT of light source   = 3800 K (= 263 MIREDs)
CT of film balanced for tungsten light = 3200 K (= 313 MIREDs).

From the relationship:

MIRED shift of filter (S) + CT of lamp in MIREDs = CT of film (in MIREDs),

we get
$$S + 313 = 182,$$
therefore
$$S = 313 - 263$$
$$= +50 \text{ MIREDs}$$

This colour temperature shift may be achieved by combining a 81D (MIRED value of +42) with an 81 (MIRED shift of +10).

The MIRED values for some commonly-used lamps and filters are given in Tables 4 and 5.

Table 4. *MIRED values for Lamps*

		Colour temperature	
Volts	Watts	Kelvins	MIREDs
6*	15	2850	351
6	30	2700	370
6*	30	3200	312
12	60	3050	328
12	100	3150	317
12 QI	100	3250	307
CSI gas discharge lamp	250	3800	263
Xenon arc (XBO)	75	5500	182

* Signifies the bulb is operated above the nominal voltage. Small departures from the nominal voltage can cause large changes in colour temperature.

Table 5. *Kodak 'Wratten' filter data*

'Wratten' number	MIRED shift
85B	+131
85	+112
85C	+81
81EF	+53
81D	+42
81C	+35
81B	+27
81A	+18
81	+10
82	−10
82A	−18
82B	−32
82C	−45
80B	−112
80A	−131

The use of the Kodak 'Wratten' series of colour temperature-correction filters has been described in detail. It should be noted, however, that several other manufacturers produce filters which are suitable for this purpose. They often use identification numbers which are based on the MIRED shift value of the filter, prefixed by a letter. Usually 'R' is used for the orange/reddish filters and 'B' for the bluish filters. Some commonly-used filters in this system are listed in Table 6, with their MIRED shift values.

Other nomenclature systems exist, which may be peculiar to individual manufacturers and their literature should be checked for details.

Table 6. *MIRED values of some commonly-used 'R' and 'B' filters*

Filter type	MIRED value
'R' filters	
R15 = R1 1/2	+15
R30 = R3	+30
R60 = R6	+60
R120 = R12	+120
'B' filters	
B120 = B12	-120
B60 = B6	-60
B30 = B3	-30
B15 = B1 1/2	-15

4.5. The use of colour compensating filters

Colour compensating filters of a varying range of densities, are produced in each of the primary colours (red, green, and blue) and also in magenta, yellow, and cyan. They are included in the 'Wratten' range manufactured by Kodak but are also available under the same numbering system from other makers. They are designated by the letters 'CC' (which stand for colour compensating), a number (which represents the optical density multiplied by 100) and a final letter which is the initial letter of the colour itself. For example we could have:

CC	**10**	**R**

which represents

Colour	Optical	Red
compensating	density = 0.1	

These filters are available in a standard range of densities in each colour, as listed in Table 7.

Colour compensating filters may be used singly or in combination as a filter pack and will give precise correction for colour casts introduced by optical components such as heat filters or polarizers or by the use of a long exposure.

One further filter which should be mentioned is made of didymium glass. This

Table 7. *Transmission of the (CC) filter range*

Filter number	Optical density
025	0.025
05	0.05
10	0.10
20	0.20
30	0.30
40	0.40
50	0.50

special glass contains a mixture of rare earth oxides and has a characteristic pinkish colour. Its transmission spectrum shows the presence of numerous narrow absorption bands, one of which coincides with the yellow sodium D line. This filter may be beneficial in the photography of stained biological specimens (especially those stained with eosin) as the magenta and pink colours are more faithfully reproduced by the colour film. The effect, however, is often unpredictable and should be verified by a series of test exposures on the actual specimens. With some specimens the improvement in colour rendering can be quite dramatic.

4.6. Reciprocity failure in colour film

Reciprocity failure (the reduction in effective film speed when very long exposures are used) already discussed for black and white films, also occurs with colour films. The chief difference is that in the case of colour emulsions, the reciprocity failure occurs independently in each of the three emulsion layers and at a different image brightness level for each layer. This may result in a change in colour balance (called **crossed curve distortion**) seen as an excess of blue in the picture; this is because the blue-sensitive layer tends to be more sensitive at lower levels of image brightness than the other two layers.

The best solution to the problem of crossed curve distortion is to use a colour film manufactured specifically for use at low light levels. One example of this type of material is Kodak 'Vericolor L' negative film, whilst a transparency film currently available which works well at lowish levels of tungsten lighting is Kodak 'Ektachrome 64T'. These films, in addition to being balanced for use in tungsten light, are designed to give correct colour rendering with exposures considerably longer than those anticipated with a film balanced for daylight. If a film intended for these longer exposures is not available and a typical daylight-balanced emulsion has to be used instead, then correction filters must be used. The manufacturer's technical data sheet will usually provide suggestions but ideally a series of trial exposures using different filters should be carried out. Such filtration is, of course, additional to any that may be required to correct for the colour temperature of the light source. This means that the light losses can become considerable and the effective film speed, therefore, may be very slow. For example, if we use 'Kodachrome 25' film in a situation which requires an exposure of more than 1 sec together with an 80A colour correction filter because we have a light source with a CT of 3200 K, then it is likely that a CC 10 M filter would be needed to counteract the effects of reciprocity failure. The result of adding these two filters would be that the effective speed of the film is reduced to about ISO 3. In the case of colour negative films, such correction can be done during the printing stage, but crossed curve distortion cannot be completely compensated for in this way. One solution, for both colour and negative film, is to take the original on one of the many high-speed colour films which are now available. These are rated at ISO 400, 600, or even 1000, and although they are inevitably rather grainier than the slower films, they often produce acceptable results. Such materials are especially valuable when taking micrographs of fluorescent specimens.

If much photomicrography is done at a low image brightness, the possibility of increasing the power of the light source should be investigated. Some high-power lighting units are available from the microscope manufacturers; alternatively, a small lighting unit may be modified by the user to accept a lamp of a much higher rating. In carrying out such modifications care should be taken to provide electrical leads, transformers and switch gear capable of handling the extra current which such lamps require. With high-power lamps, cooling is another important aspect which should not be ignored. Not only is there a risk of heat damage to the specimen, but optical components such as polarizers and phase rings may be destroyed by an excessive temperature rise. The use of heat-absorbing glass filters is essential in such situations although it should be remembered that these often introduce a greenish colour cast which requires correcting with CC filters. As an alternative, the use of the old-fashioned water cell in the illumination train (if there is sufficient room), may provide an acceptable and very simple heat barrier. In both cases, it may also be necessary to provide some form of fan cooling for the lamp and the lamp house.

It should not be forgotten that many manufacturers of colour film (as well as independent processing laboratories) now provide a service whereby colour films may be uprated, that is exposed at a doubled or even quadrupled ISO rating. This increase in the film speed is then compensated for by giving extra time in the first development; this is often called **push processing** and is much used in fluorescence micrography (see Chapter 6).

5

Photomacrography

In general photography the object to be recorded is usually large and at some considerable distance from the camera. Its image on the film, therefore, is much smaller than the object itself. If the object is small it must be brought close to the camera lens, which is moved away from the film plane in order to form a sharp image which may be larger than the object itself. The expression

$$\frac{\text{Image size}}{\text{Object size}}$$

is called the **reproduction ratio** (which refers to the *negative*, unless otherwise stated). This ratio may be expressed as a multiplier (e.g. $0.1\times$; $0.5\times$; $1\times$; $10\times$; etc.) where the image was one-tenth, one-half, the same size or ten times larger than the object size, respectively. Alternatively, the same series could be written as: 1:10; 1:2; 1:1; 10:1. If prints are made, then further magnification may be introduced which should be described separately as the **degree of enlargement** and included in the technical data of the micrograph, along with the reproduction ratio. A better practice is to add to the print a marker bar which is labelled to indicate the length that it would represent in the original object.

Most cameras when fitted with a standard focal length lens focused at its nearest distance give a reproduction ratio of about $0.1\times$ (1:10). It is possible to increase this ratio by adding a close-up lens or by using extension tubes. By convention, this is called **close-up photography** when the reproduction ratios are between 1:10 and 1:1. If the reproduction ratio is further increased from, say, 1:1 to 20:1 (i.e. the magnification on the film is $20\times$), then the technique is called **photomacrography**. Objects for which we use these special techniques are usually too large to be viewed with the compound microscope but may easily be studied with the stereomicroscope. When photographs are taken with either a stereomicroscope or a standard compound microscope then we are carrying out **photomicrography**. The distinctions between *close-up photography* and *photomacrography* are fine and often a matter of arbitrary definition. In general, the techniques of photomicrography (using a compound microscope) are used when the reproduction ratio exceeds 20:1 and are satisfactory up to a reproduction ratio of perhaps 2000:1. Above this figure, **electron microscopy** must be used if further resolution and magnification are desired.

Macrophotography is traditionally performed with a camera system in which the distance between the film plane and the lens (the extension) may be increased by large amounts, often by means of a bellows unit when a larger than life-size image is required.

In conventional photography the extension is much less than the distance between the lens and the object itself, hence camera lenses are designed to give high-quality images when used in this way. With large extensions (when the distance between the film plane and the lens becomes much greater than that between the lens and the object itself in order to obtain a reproduction ratio of, say, 15:1), the image formed by a standard camera lens is often of poor quality. This is largely due to spherical aberration introduced by the unusual degree of extension. In such circumstances, if a normal lens must be used, the image quality may be greatly improved by simply reversing the lens, so that the surface which normally faces the film plane now faces the object. The special adaptors for this use the screw thread on the front of the lens (normally intended to hold filters) for the reverse mounting onto the bellows or extension tubes. Additional accessories are available to operate the automatic iris diaphragm when the lens is used in this way. With long extensions and a reversed camera lens, the relative positions of object and image more closely match those for which the lens was designed and hence the aberrations are less with a much improved image quality (Fig. 11).

5.1. Camera lenses with close focus capability

These lenses are now being produced for users of single lens reflex cameras. Many 'zoom' lenses feature a close focus 'macro' capability and some fixed focal length lenses (such as the Micro Nikkors) can focus an object located from infinity to a few inches away without the use of extension tubes. Such lenses are often manufactured with the lens elements deeply recessed into the mount, so that no extra lens hood is necessary, a valuable feature when working close to an object. Most of these lenses intended for 35-mm format cameras have a focal length of 55 mm, but some are available with longer focal lengths. These latter, although more expensive, have the advantage that for a given reproduction ratio the lens is further from the object than if a shorter focal length lens were in use; it is thus much easier to arrange suitable lighting of the specimen. Such close-focus lenses serve very well when the reproduction ratio does not exceed 1:1 and are thus very convenient for many situations in the laboratory and in the field.

5.2. Stereomicroscopes

Stereomicroscopes are available from many makers, and are frequently fitted with a zoom facility for changing the magnification. If a trinocular head or a camera tube is fitted then these instruments can be used for taking pictures in the range covered by photomacrography. The units may be fitted with a trans-illumination base, often with bright and dark-ground capabilities and for incident lighting of specimens an axial illuminator is usually available as an accessory. In many cases, however, the illumination of opaque specimens will be carried out by some form of oblique lighting either from microscope spotlights or from fibre optic units. This latter form of illumination may also be supplied in the form of a ring illuminator for axial shadowless lighting. If the camera tube can be moved from one optical axis

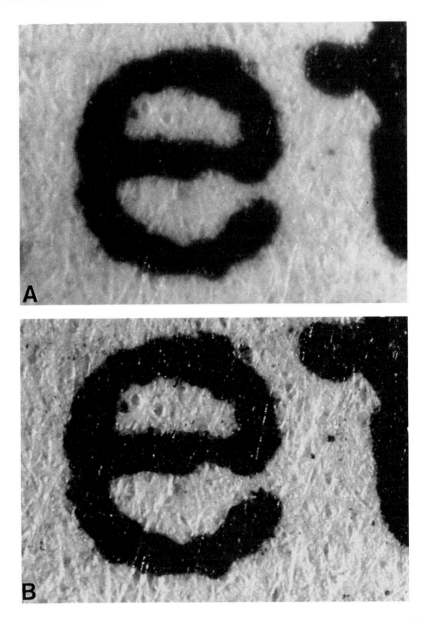

Fig. 11. A photomacrograph of the letter e on a sheet of typescript, at a magnification of 8.5×
on the film. This was taken with a Nikon F2 camera, with a bellows extension of 43 cm and the
standard 50-mm f2 lens. (A) was taken with the lens in its normal orientation; the image is not
sharp and of low contrast due to spherical aberration introduced by the extreme lens-film distance. (B) the lens has been reversed; note the increased contrast and image sharpness apparent
with this mode of working which more closely resembles the conditions for which the corrections of the lens were computed.

to the other, then very impressive and informative stereo pair photographs may be produced.

5.3. Special-purpose photomacrographic systems

Several vertical bellows macro-camera systems have been produced commercially, e.g. the 'Aristophot' from Leitz and the Nikon 'Multiphot'. These have large format or 35-mm facilities and accessories for transmitted or reflected-light work. They usually have a complete range of matched macro lenses and condensers and are solidly-built and versatile. In the absence of a large-format camera mounted on a special rail screwed to the wall (as outlined in the survey article by Bracegirdle, 1983) the use of equipment such as the 'Multiphot' is perhaps the most satisfactory way of achieving consistently good photomacrographs. Older, similar equipment which is no longer in production may be available in many laboratories and could still be used to good effect.

There are other macro systems available in which the magnification is controlled by the use of zoom optics rather than by varying the extension of bellows. The Wild 'M400 PhotoMakroskop' and the Zeiss 'Tessovar' are probably the two best known of such systems. The Wild system has its own automatic camera system which gives full automatic control over the exposure. The 'Tessovar', a 4:1 zoom system with interchangeable objectives, has a range of camera units or adaptors for a number of still, cine or TV cameras. Its lenses, however, have too low a numerical aperture to give the very highest-quality results when operated in the transmitted-light mode. The Tessovar is fitted with a zoom magnification control coupled to the iris aperture diaphragm, so that constant image brightness is achieved throughout the zoom range, hence minimizing exposure problems.

5.4. Special lenses for photomacrography

Several special lenses are available for photomacrography. They are designed to produce good images at long camera extensions and short object distances. Examples are the Zeiss 'Luminars', the Leitz 'Summars', the 'Macro-Nikkors' of Nikon, and the 'Auto Macro Zuiko' lenses of Olympus. Such lenses are produced in a range of focal lengths so that a wide range of magnifications may be achieved. The 'Macro-Nikkors', for example, have focal lengths of 120 mm, 65 mm, 35 mm, and 19 mm which give reproduction ratios ranging from 1:3 to 40:1 in the 35-mm format.

As with microscope objectives, the resolving power of such macro lenses *decreases* as the aperture of the lens is reduced, although the depth of field is *increased*. This must be borne in mind when the working aperture is chosen, as although stopping down the lens will increase the depth of field, this is only achieved at the expense of some loss of resolution of specimen fine detail. This effect becomes more prominent as the reproduction ratio (magnification) increases. In general, the iris diaphragm of specialist macro lenses should not be closed more than one division. If it is necessary to obtain more depth of field, then the effect of further closure should be critically studied using a focusing magnifier to view the image on the camera ground-glass screen. Any apparent thickening of fine line structures in the specimen or increasing size of small highlights are typical indicators that the aperture of the lens has been reduced too much.

5.5. Problems in close-up photography and photomacrography

5.5.1. *Depth of field*

If a lens is focused on a given plane then, in theory, objects in that plane will be absolutely sharp. In practice, because of diffraction of the light and because of lens aberrations, each point in the object is represented not by a point but by a small circle termed the **circle of confusion**. For any given viewing distance the eye can only resolve detail of a certain size; if the circle of confusion is equal to, or less, than this size then details in the image will appear crisp and sharp. Points which are nearer to and further away from the plane of focus will produce slightly larger images, but there will be a zone on either side of the plane of focus in which the detail is recorded sufficiently sharply for it to be indistinguishable from that in the plane of exact focus. This zone of sharp focus is called the **depth of field**. It varies with the focal length of the lens, the subject distance and the f-aperture of the lens, so that a longer focal length, a closer subject distance and a larger f-aperture will all decrease the zone in which detail is acceptably sharp. The focal length and the subject distance are, of course, involved in the determination of the reproduction ratio; the higher this ratio (i.e. the greater the magnification of the image) the smaller will be the depth of field. Tables of depth of field are available in the literature, calculated for lenses of various focal lengths used at various apertures and degrees of magnification. Such tables are usually based on a circle of confusion of 0.01 mm for the 35-mm format. Alternatively, the depth of field may be calculated from a formula given in most photographic reference books. For a 50-mm lens focused on a plane 3 m away and used at an aperture of f2, the depth of field would be about 0.144 m (144 mm); the same lens, used at the same aperture but focused on a plane 5 cm away (giving a reproduction ratio of 4:1) would have a depth of field of only 0.04 m!

The depth of field, although it can be expressed numerically, assuming a given size for the circle of confusion, is a very subjective quality. The apparent sharpness of the image is also affected by such factors as the photographic grain, any possible blur due to subject or camera movement, and to image defects introduced by aberrations in the lens. As it is necessary to increase the depth of field as much as possible, the lens must be stopped down as much as practicable, although with some macro lenses this would impair the resolution. The effect, on the depth of field, of stopping down a macro lens is illustrated in Fig. 12. It is clear from this figure that the lack of depth of field in the phtomacrography of three-dimensional objects at large reproduction ratios poses a major problem. If swing and tilt movements on the lens panel and on the film back are available, as in some professional

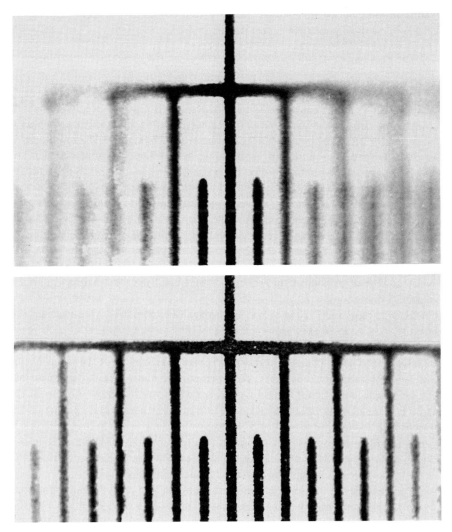

Fig. 12. A photograph of a millimetre scale to show the effect of stopping down on the depth of field in photomacrography. The scale was inclined at an angle of 45° to the optical axis of the camera and both exposures were made with a reversed 50-mm lens and 20 cm of bellows extension. The upper exposure, at a nominal aperture of f2.8, has a very shallow depth of field; this is increased (but only to a limited extent) when the nominal aperture is reduced to f22, as shown in the lower illustration.

view cameras and one or two of the more expensive 35-mm system bellows, then the overall sharpness may be dramatically increased. Swinging or tilting either (or both) the lens panel or the film holder will utilize the effect of what is called the **Scheimpflug Principle** to increase the sharpness dramatically without resorting to extreme degrees of stopping down the lens. Full details of this technique will be found in manuals of photographic technique.

5.5.2. *Perspective distortions and problems when using large reproduction ratios*

In many cases, in order to obtain the required magnification of the image, it is necessary to use a lens of short focal length which must approach the object very closely. In such circumstances, gross perspective distortions may occur. This is well known when using short-focus lenses for general photography and is often used deliberately in order to obtain grotesque effects. The distortion is less noticeable in macro work (and is not present with subjects in which the principal plane of interest lies in a plane parallel to the film plane); the only solution to the problem is to use a macro lens of longer focal length which allows a greater distance between the specimen and the camera, so reducing the distortion. It may then be necessary to record the image at a reduced reproduction ratio and obtain the desired final magnification by photographic enlargement; with the exceedingly fine grain of films such as Kodak 'Technical Pan 2415', this is a perfectly satisfactory solution and it will at the same time give an image with an increased depth of field. Again, the use of camera or bellows movements, if they are fitted, will help to minimize perspective distortions.

With large reproduction ratios (i.e. high magnifications) it is often necessary to use quite long bellows extensions, perhaps of the order of 30 cm. In such cases, vibrations due to minute movements of the mechanical parts of the system may be a significant problem, as they can result in appreciable blurring of the image on the film. The only cure is to use very stable support systems. It is also possible that with long extensions significant vibrations may be introduced by the rise of the mirror in a single lens reflex (SLR) camera body just before the opening of the shutter. With modern, high-quality SLRs this is less of a problem than in the early days of this type of camera, but it can be totally prevented by locking the mirror up after focusing and before releasing the shutter. The use of electronic flash also materially helps reduce image blurring due to mechanical vibrations.

The reduced levels of illumination often found at high reproduction ratios may cause focusing problems. In many cameras it is possible to replace the focusing screen with one which has a clear area bearing engraved cross lines. These are imaged with a magnifier at the same time as the image, which can then easily be brought into focus. Focusing should be carried out at the largest aperture possible and the lens stopped down to its working aperture just before exposure. With some systems a double cable release is available which with one press of the release will stop down the camera lens immediately before the shutter is released. When focusing at given reproduction ratios remember that the extension of the bellows governs the reproduction ratio. This means that adjustment of the focus should not be achieved with the rackwork mechanism of the bellows, as is often the practice. Instead, the whole set-up should be moved bodily towards, or away from, the subject until this latter is in sharp focus. Special camera platforms fitted with low-geared rackwork are available for this purpose; if much photomacrography is carried out at given reproduction ratios then such an accessory is very valuable. Setting a given reproduction ratio is often done very easily and directly by using the markings engraved on the lens barrel or on the base of the bellows. If such markings are not provided on your equipment, then it is well worth copying a **reproduction-ratio ruler** at the same size on photographic paper which is then mounted onto card. This ruler is then imaged in the viewfinder and the reproduction ratio set from its calibrations. A drawing of such a rule is given in the book by Lefkowitz (1979).

5.5.3. *Exposure problems*

Many workers find that the calculation of the correct exposure is the most difficult part of photomacrography. Often the close subject-to-lens distances make the use of standard photographic exposure meters difficult and in many cases, because of the large extensions involved, the light levels reaching the film plane will be low and the exposures therefore necessarily prolonged, possibly leading to problems with film reciprocity failure. With modern 35-mm cameras having **through-the-lens metering** (TTL) many of the problems disappear, since such exposure metering takes into account the fall-off in illumination intensity as the extension is increased. Some of the more sophisticated systems will be provided with an automatic diaphragm control which operates even when extension tubes and bellows are fitted. Other systems require the use of a special adapter ring and a double cable release which closes the lens diaphragm to the taking aperture immediately prior to releasing the shutter. In both of these instances, therefore, metering is carried out at the maximum aperture of the camera lens thus allowing the best possible viewing conditions right up to the actual moment of exposure. If automatic diaphragm operation is not available, as is often the case if macro lenses are in use, the system is operated in what is usually called a 'stop-down' mode. In this, the aperture of the lens is manually set after which the exposure meter will either indicate, or actually set, the required exposure. Some 35-mm cameras now available measure the exposure not from light falling onto sensors fitted into the viewing head or camera body but from the light reflected from the shutter blind or from the film itself (**OTF metering**). These systems lend themselves well to macro work and many have the advantage that the same method of metering works with a dedicated electronic flash unit.

It should be noted that the aperture marked on the lens mount, if it is a standard camera lens used on bellows or extension tubes, will not in this case correspond to the actual aperture at which the macrograph is taken. The actual or **effective aperture** may be calculated from the equation:

$$\text{Effective aperture} = \text{Nominal aperture} \times (\text{Mag.} + 1).$$

Similarly, the effective increase in the required exposure may be calculated. This is given by the relationship:

$$\text{Exposure increase} = (\text{Mag.} + 1)^2.$$

Thus for a reproduction ratio of 1:1 (i.e. an extension of 50 mm with a camera lens of 50 mm focal length) a 4X increase of exposure is needed in comparison with that required for a photograph taken with the same lens focused at infinity. In photographic terms this exposure increase of 4X represents two f-stops. An increase of 8X would be three f-stops, 6X would be four stops, and 32X would represent five stops increase of exposure.

If a large-format camera is in use it is often possible to take an exposure reading directly from the focusing screen using either a meter such as the Gossen 'Microsix', 'Profisix' or 'Lunasix' or by substituting a 'Sinarsix' meter with its movable probe in place of the film dark slide. All of these give readings over a limited area and are similar, therefore, to the spot-metering mode of many 35-mm cameras. Some integrating meters (such as the Beuhler exposure computer) are available for large-format cameras and these work extremely well in the majority of situations, especially where the bulk of the field is occupied by the specimen. With integrated metering, it is as well to remember that such methods are intended to give accurate results on a subject with average reflectiveness. This may not be true for many of the subjects encountered in photomacrography and hence, if accurate and consistent exposures are required from an integrated method of metering, it is often advisable to take the reading from a Kodak grey card of standard 18 percent reflectiveness which is temporarily substituted for the subject.

In photomacrography, even with all the automated aids to success which are available today, it is still true that experience is invaluable. This is especially important for obtaining consistent and accurate exposures. A great help towards this end is the keeping of accurate records at the time of exposure; such records should be as complete as possible and will in many cases serve as a valuable supplement to the readings provided by the apparatus. In photomacrography, the setting up of the specimen and the adjustment of the lighting, achieving the correct reproduction ratio, etc., are very time-consuming. It is advisable, therefore, if there is any doubt about the correctness of the exposure, to take several more shots, 'bracketing' the estimated correct exposure with additional longer and shorter exposures. The latitude of black and white film is considerable, so that these exposures should differ markedly from the correct estimate; with colour film with its much smaller latitude the bracketing exposures may well differ from the estimate by only two-thirds of a f-stop. Film is generally cheaper than the microscopist's time which would be required to duplicate the shots from scratch. If at all possible (especially when working with large-format material) it is a good practice to leave a macro set-up undisturbed until the exposures have been processed. In this way, a repeat is relatively easy to achieve, should it be required.

5.5.4. *Problems of lighting a macro specimen*

The problems involved here are perhaps even more daunting to many workers than the determination of the correct exposure! Consideration must be given to the evenness and possibly to the colour temperature of the lighting, as well as to the size, shape, and texture of opaque objects which may require emphasis by the lighting. The basic requirements are that the light sources shall be bright, small, easily moved, and fixed in the required positions. Standard studio lighting equipment is generally much too large and often produces too much heat to be of any use in photomacrography.

The older type of low-voltage microscope lamp is a very useful illuminant for macroscopic work. Most of these lights possess a focusable collector lens which allows them to serve as mini spotlights for macro work. Care must be taken when using this type of lamp in order to avoid imaging the filament onto the specimen and so producing uneven lighting in the form of bright and dark stripes crossing the field of view. An extra lens installed in a tube attached to the front of one of these old lamps will produce a uniform bright disc of light (in fact an image of the lamp collector lens itself, acting as a secondary light source) which gives even illumination for photomacrography. This resembles the optical arrangement of a theatre 'follow spot' and produces hard shadows and brilliant highlights, of value in the demonstration of surface texture.

Another good type of light for photomacrography is the **fibre optic illuminator**. These consist of a light source (usually a 12V QI lamp) in a case together with a cooling fan and a socket into which various different fibre optic bundles may be plugged. Some of these bundles are single-headed, others are dual-headed and a multi-headed version is also available. In addition there is a ring head which may be fixed around the macro lens to produce very even lighting, similar to that given by the older multiple-lamp ring illuminator. Fibre optic illimunators are valuable because they give an intense light without heat. There use is not without problems; for example, some fibre optic heads are difficult to position accurately due to the stiffness of the metal sheath of the fibre bundle, and the power unit is heavy and often difficult to move about. Injudicious placing of this unit may result in the air from the cooling fan actually blowing the specimen away at the crucial moment! Lawrence (1980) has provided useful information on the use of fibre optic light guides in photomacrography.

The photomacrography of specimens by transmitted light often presents problems; ideally one would wish to use a Köhler-type illuminating system as on the microscope but capable of illuminating a much larger area in the specimen plane. Such a device (known as a **diascopic illuminator**) is available from Nikon, Leitz, and Olympus. These units consist of a focusing stage for the specimen with a large-diameter condenser mounted below it and illuminated by means of a large mirror mounted at 45° to the optical axis together with a lamp carried on a horizontal rail. A number of separate top elements of the condenser are provided to match the focal lengths of the macro lenses. In use, the illuminator is centred under the vertically-mounted camera and the correct top element of the condenser lens fitted. The lamp is then adjusted to produce an image of its filament in the plane of the iris diaphragm of the macro lens. It is important that the macro lens is at the correct distance above the top condenser lens and some systems make this easy by marking the column of the macro stand in a suitable manner. If a diascopic illuminator is not available, it is often possible to use some form of diffuse light source (e.g. an X-ray viewer fitted with an opal glass) or an inverted enlarger lamp housing. The use of these is described in Bracegirdle (1983), a valuable reference source for workers in this field.

It is possible to obtain transmitted light dark-ground illumination suitable for photomacrography by using off-axis illumination from below the specimen stage. This may be provided by several spot lamps, by an inverted ring illuminator or even an inverted camera ring flash unit (Fig. 13). With such an arrangement, black velvet or some other non-reflecting black material placed a few inches below the specimen will absorb any light reflected from its underside and ensure a truly dark background.

The possible variants of incident lighting for photomacrography of opaque specimens are many, and the chief need is to be able to improvise and experiment, observing the effect of any changes carefully in the viewfinder or on the ground glass of the camera. The simplest type of lighting is oblique incident, which is best provided by spotlights or fibre optic units mounted above, and to one side of, the specimen. It is usually necessary to lighten the strong shadows which are produced either by using a small reflector of aluminium foil or a second, lower-powered light on the other side (Fig. 14). In some cases the structure of the specimen will best be shown by some form of near-axial lighting. This may be achieved by means of a half-mirror attachment (available as an accessory for some systems) or, more cheaply, by mounting a thin sheet of clean glass at 45° immediately below the camera lens. In both cases, the light is from a spotlight mounted at right angles to the optical axis of the camera (Fig. 15). A similar shadowless form of lighting uses a Lieberkühn type of mirror; here the light comes from below, surrounding the specimen and parallel with the optical axis, and is reflected down onto the specimen by the mirror. Only the light reflected by the specimen is used to form the image, any direct light being excluded by means of the central opaque stop (Fig. 16). It is quite easy to improvise such Lieberkühn mirrors from reflectors taken from discarded torches. Perhaps the most common form of shadowless incident lighting now in use is the fibre optic ring illuminator already mentioned. These are efficient, simple to use and give a much brighter light than the other techniques just mentioned.

Most forms of tungsten light sources are adequate for black and white work, but for colour photography the colour temperature of the illuminant must also be taken into consideration. Any of the lighting methods described above will, if they use QI bulbs operated at the correct voltage, provide light at a colour temperature which is suitable for use with artificial-light colour film. It should be remembered that reducing the voltage of such lamps not only reduces their intensity and greatly extends their lifetime but also makes them emit at a lower colour temperature (i.e. the light is richer in the longer wavelengths). This can be corrected by suitable filtration on the camera provided that the user knows the approximate colour temperature of the light. In practice very few users have access to a colour temperature meter, so that they have to rely on estimates. If the voltage at which the QI bulb is running is known, then a rough guess at the colour temperature may be

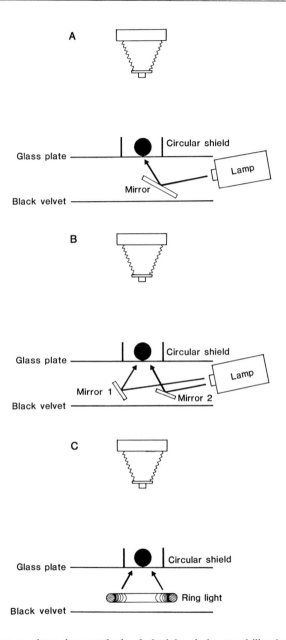

Fig. 13. A diagram to show three methods of obtaining dark ground illumination for photo-macrography. In all cases the object is on a glass plate fixed several inches above a black velvet background and is surrounded by a circular shield covered on its inner face with the same material. The extreme oblique illumination is obtained in (A) by a spotlight and one mirror, whilst in (B) a second mirror is added to even out the illumination. Set-up (C) uses an inverted ring light to provide all round oblique illumination of the specimen.

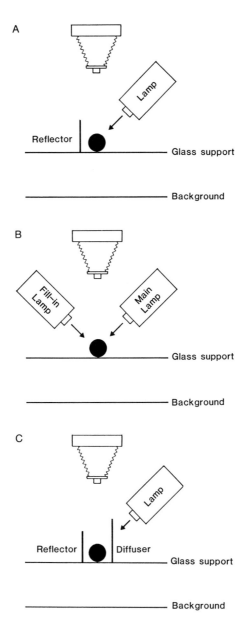

Fig. 14. Various methods of achieving incident oblique illumination for photomacrography. The illustration (A) shows a single spotlamp with a small reflector placed on the opposite side to lighten the strong shadows formed in this technique. An improvement is to use a lower-powered fill-in lamp arranged opposite the main lamp (B). If only one lamp is available, then an improvement on the original lighting arrangement is to add a diffuser between the lamp and the object(C).

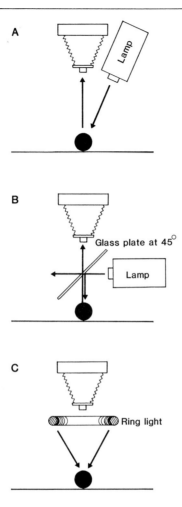

Fig. 15. A diagram to show various methods of achieving near-axial illumination. With long focus lenses, when the camera to object distance is considerable, a spotlamp may be mounted alongside the camera as shown in (A). Better results are often obtained by reflecting the light onto the object from a thin sheet of glass mounted at 45° to the optical axis of the lens, as shown in (B); as a large amount of light is lost the exposures often tend to be rather long. A ring light mounted around the lens as shown in (C) is a very effective solution to the problem.

made using data published in an article by Jenny and Panozzo-Heilbronner (1981a). They indicate that a Philips 12V/100W QI bulb operated at 12 V has a colour temperature of 3250 K; reducing the voltage to 10 V brings the colour temperature down to 3050 K, whilst at 8 V the colour temperature falls to 2825 K and at 6 V it is only 2550 K. In the same article, advice is given on the correct filtration to use for obtaining correct colour balance with fluorescent ring lights.

Lighting opaque subjects from above may prove difficult if shadows are thrown onto a light-coloured background. Such a problem may usually be remedied by

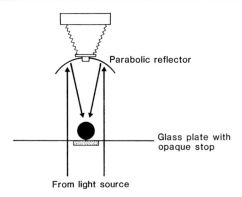

Parabolic reflector

Glass plate with
opaque stop

From light source

Fig. 16. Axial lighting from a Lieberkühn mirror mounted around the lens. In this method the light comes from below the specimen but direct transmitted light is prevented from entering the system by mounting the object on an opaque stop.

mounting the specimen on a clear glass support bridge which is held several centimetres above the background. If the angle of the lighting is not too steep (i.e. very close to the optical axis of the camera) then the shadows will fall onto the background outside the field of view of the camera. Jenny and Palozzo-Heilbronner (1981b) give some useful hints on techniques of incident illumination.

Another difficulty which often arises when lighting specimens for macrography is the prevention of specular reflections from the surface of highly-polished objects. Two techniques are worth remembering in such instances. One is to immerse the object entirely in some clear fluid such as water or glycerol before taking the photograph. This will often remove the reflection although possibly at the expense of damage to the object and the risk of marring the micrograph by small bubbles which often form in the immersion medium. A more satisfactory solution to the problem of specular reflection is to place the object inside a **light tent** which is an open-topped cone or hemisphere of some white translucent material. If a light tent is strongly illuminated on its outer surface (Fig. 17) then the specimen inside will be lit evenly and the specular reflections are abolished. Such light tents are often made as required from white typing paper, but for small objects they may be made from half of a ping-pong ball with a hole cut in it for the lens; on occasion a small light tent may even be made from part of an eggshell.

The possibilities for different lighting set-ups are considerable; readers interested in photomacrography are encouraged first to read some of the excellent books which are available on the subject (e.g. Blaker 1977; Brück 1984; Angel 1983; Lefkowitz 1979; Croy 1961) and secondly to experiment with their own specimens and equipment.

5.5.5. *Problems associated with the support of the subject and the camera*

The principal difficulties with the support of the camera are usually concerned with preventing vibrations affecting the sharpness of the image. As the reproduction

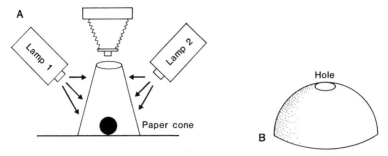

Fig. 17. (A) A diagram to show how a light tent made from a paper cone is used in order to obtain even lighting of an object which shows many specular reflections in its surface. (B) For very small objects a light tent may be made from half of a ping-pong ball in which a hole has been made, as shown.

ratio increases and extensions get longer, this becomes more significant than at low image magnifications. Many of the camera manufacturers produce small so-called **macro stands** which are intended to support the camera and its bellows; at the same time they often provide a rudimentary form of specimen stage. These are not sufficiently rigid for professional use or when the reproduction ratio exceeds about 2:1, but may be useful for the occasional photograph in the laboratory or when the specimen cannot be taken into the photographic studio. If much photomacrography is intended then one of the larger stands such as the Leitz 'Aristophot' or the Nikon 'Multiphot' is required. Alternatively, as recommended by Bracegirdle (1983), a special rail may be fixed to the wall to carry a bellows camera which is dedicated to photomacrography.

It is worth noting that the photographic accessory manufacturers produce a multiplicity of gadgets (intended for amateur use) which are more or less successful at their intended job of holding a camera with some form of close-focus attachment. Most of these are intended for field use and include for example a spike (about 150 mm in length) which carries a tripod-bush screw on the top, and is intended for driving into the ground to support the camera at low level. Small tripods abound, but most are too flimsy for serious use; one camera-mounting device is available with a powerful suction base intended to clamp to smooth flat surfaces, whilst another has as its base a very powerful magnet. These can be very useful in certain circumstances, as can the holding device mounted onto a G-clamp, that mounted onto a large wood screw, and yet another intended to be secured to 10-mm diameter laboratory scaffold tubing. All of these are useful at times, especially if they are fitted with a *sturdy* ball and socket head.

Similar problems are met in supporting the specimen. A vertically-mounted camera system is generally the most convenient for photomacrography and it is very helpful to have a specimen stage that can be raised and lowered for the final focusing. Ideally, with short focal length macro lenses, such a stage should have a precision motion similar to the fine focus of a microscope stage. Such are not available commercially, but the resourceful photomacrographer can often construct such a stage if components from a discarded microscope come to hand. Even with a suitable stage the specimen itself has to be secured from movement throughout the alignment process and the exposure. The secret is not to be afraid to improvise. 'Plasticine' and 'Blu-tack' are invaluable (though their tendency to soften under the prolonged heat of photo lights must be remembered!) as well as paper-clips and supports fashioned, as the occasion demands, from thin wire. If any stage forceps are available from an old microscope then they can usefully be pressed into service for holding small objects. Another interesting device is the hemispherical base; an object mounted in the centre of one of these does not move out of the optic axis of the system when the stage is tilted. Such a hemispherical base (sometimes called a 'cup stage') may be purchased, but one is easily made (Bracegirdle 1983). Many suggestions for specimen holding may be found in the literature and as each object presents its own new challenge to the photographer there is great scope for experiment in this aspect of photomacrography.

Cine and fluorescence micrography; instant print systems

6.1. Cine and video photomicrography

Occasionally a film unit which does not specialize in scientific work visits the laboratory with the intention of recording microscopical images on cine film or video tape. When this happens the chaos that ensues can be remarkable, especially if the director of the production is highly creative in the artistic sense but is non-technical in approach!

One of the first problems encountered is that of camera support. Most self-blimped 16-mm units are of considerable weight and the majority of commercial photographic tripods are not able to provide the necessary mechanical rigidity for this type of camera. Similar considerations apply even to the modern light-weight video cameras. It is also quite likely that the tripods normally used by the film crew will not allow the camera to be installed over the microscope. In these circumstances, the best solution is to fix the cine or video camera above the microscope by mounting it on a substantial stand such as that formerly available from the firm of Wild. Alternatively, the Leitz 'Aristophot' or the Nikon 'Multiphot' type of stand can often be adapted to serve as a suitable camera support. Most commercial enlarger or copy stands currently available would, however, not be of sufficient rigidity.

Once the mechanical support problems have been solved, the optical problems (which can also be severe) may be considered. If the filming is an isolated event, then an acceptable image may be obtained by removing the camera zoom lens and inserting the eyepiece tube of the microscope into the lens opening. If the film camera has a rotating mirror shutter (such as that in the 'Arriflex') care is needed to ensure that the eyepiece of the microscope does not touch the mirror. After carefully aligning the microscope–camera combination it is possible to produce an image on the film plane by radically re-focusing the microscope. This is bad technique but sometimes it is the only way in which essential pictures may be obtained. The results, with care, may be quite acceptable. If a projection eyepiece is available, then this should be substituted for the standard microscope eyepiece as the resulting image in the film plane will be of much higher quality (see Section 1.1).

The above technique may be used on the rare occasions of the one-off film sequence. For serious cine photomicrography it is obviously desirable to use equipment which is designed for that specific purpose. Most manufacturers supply special cine adaptors with the associated rigid stands needed to build a solid system. For most purposes, 100 feet spool-loading 16-mm cameras are the most convenient; the 'Bolex H16 series or the 'Beaulieu R16' with C-mount lens fittings are used by many workers. The 'Beaulieu R16' is electrically driven, whilst the 'Bolex' is available in two versions. One has clockwork drive with the ability to accept an add-on electric motor, whilst the other model has a built-in electric drive. 'Through-the-lens' metering is a very useful facility in cine photomicrography, whilst 'through-the-lens' viewing is essential for accurate framing of the image.

The high-speed colour reversal film stock produced for TV news applications is very suitable for cine photomicrography; it is balanced for a colour temperature of 3200 K and is rated nominally at ASA 125, with the capability of speed increase by 'push processing' if required. This latter feature is useful when light intensity is low, e.g. with phase-contrast microscopy at a high magnification. Illumination will usually be by means of QI lamps which, when run at the correct voltage, will give a close approximation to the correct colour temperature. Problems may arise if discharge lamps are used. These lamps flicker at the supply frequency (50 Herz in the U.K.) which is twice the framing rate (24 or 25 frames per second) for sound speed on cine intended for TV use. The problem due to the flicker of discharge lamps shows itself in the finished film as a slow, regular increase and decrease in image brightness due to strobing of the lamp flicker frequency by the camera shutter. The effect may be eliminated by filming at higher frame rates than normal if the resultant slowing down of the motion on the screen is not a problem. It is possible for flicker to result when using filament lamps, but this is much less common. The problem may be overcome by using a D.C. supply for the lamp, using either a rectifier unit or a 12-V car battery. If a rectifier unit is used it must be capable of delivering the necessary power; a 12-V, 100 W QI lamp, for example, will need a supply of at least 10 A. With either a power pack or a car battery as the supply, it is useful to have a control resistance in series with the lamp so that the current may be adjusted to a measured standard value for each shot. If the lamp is being under-run slightly, then some filtration will be required to correct the colour temperature.

Video microscopy is now much used for teaching and for recording onto video tape. The problems associated with camera support are similar to those encountered in cine-micrography but there is an added complication. Video cameras have small tubes (often only ½ inch in diameter), so that the image area displayed on the monitor when they are used with standard microscope lenses is very small as compared to the image area seen through the eyepiece. It has been calculated that with a standard wide field eyepiece (field of view number = 18) the visual field corresponds to 254 mm^2 of the primary image. If a TV camera with a ½ inch tube is placed 125 mm above the same eyepiece and the microscope re-focused to produce a sharp image, then only 1 mm^2 of the primary image will be displayed on the monitor. In addition, the image will be of low quality. The solution to this problem is to connect the microscope to the TV camera with correctly-designed projection optics having a suitably low magnification (e.g. about 0.45X. If this is done, an area of the primary image of about 122 mm² may then be displayed on the monitor.

6.2. Instant print systems

The use of **'Polaroid' instant print** films in technical photography has been well established for many years, not only because these materials allow for rapid checks on the exposure and composition to be made, but also because they often have other features which make them valuable to the photographer. Nowadays, all microscope manufacturers produce adapters which allow the use of 'Polaroid' films in their photomicrographic cameras; usually there is the choice of either $3\frac{1}{4} \times 4\frac{1}{4}$ inch eight-exposure film packs or single sheet 5×4 inch materials. Adaptors are also available to enable both sizes to be used with an international 5×4 inch back or in a Hasselblad roll-film camera. The MP4 technical camera made by 'Polaroid' itself operates as a vertical macro system or it can be adapted to fit any microscope with a vertical tube.

The types of 'Polaroid' film most commonly used in photomicrography are listed in Table 8.

Table 8. *Some Polaroid instant films*

Film number	Size*	ISO speed	Film type**
T668	$3\frac{1}{4} \times 4\frac{1}{4}$	80	Daylight colour
T669	$3\frac{1}{4} \times 4\frac{1}{4}$	80	Daylight colour ER
T665	$3\frac{1}{4} \times 4\frac{1}{4}$	75	Daylight colour ER
T667	$3\frac{1}{4} \times 4\frac{1}{4}$	3000	Daylight colour ER
T59	5×4	80	Daylight colour ER
T55	5×4	50	Black and white; Print + negative
T52	5×4	400	Black and white print
T57	5×4	3000	Black and white print
T51	5×4	125	Blue-sensitive only; high contrast
'Polapan'	35 mm	125	Black and white transparency
'Polachrome'	35 mm	40	Colour transparency

 * In inches unless stated otherwise.
** ER = extended range.

The 'Polaroid SX70' single lens reflex camera may also be used with a special adaptor on any microscope to produce $3\frac{1}{4} \times 4$ inch colour prints on Type T778 film, rated at ISO 150. For the small-scale user, this is a very convenient way to produce colour prints from any available microscope. All the 'Polaroid' colour films are balanced for daylight, so that colour temperature correction by means of filters is required. Further filtration is also needed to compensate for reciprocity failure if the exposure times become long and full details of this are included in the instruction sheet packaged with the film. It is worth noting that the T668 colour film has a slightly higher contrast than either the T59 or T669 films; this may be an advantage with some types of specimen.

The black and white films all have panchromatic sensitization, with the exception of T51, which is blue-sensitive only. This means that contrast control with colour filters is possible with most 'Polaroid' black and white films. The two positive/negative films (T55 and T665) produce an instant black and white print together with a negative which requires treatment in 12 per cent sodium sulphite solution before washing and drying. After this, the negative may be enlarged and printed by conventional methods. Of these two materials, the T665 gives a negative of somewhat higher contrast than that from T55, even though it is rated at a slightly higher speed.

It is apparent that a wide range of sensitive materials is available and new emulsions are added constantly. When results are needed rapidly and there is no access to a darkroom a suitable film may be found from the Polaroid range for almost any need. Slide printers which give an instant colour print from any 35-mm colour slide are now available and these are useful when prints need producing from original transparencies in a hurry.

Recently Polaroid have produced a system of instant 35-mm films which have some applications in photomicrography. After exposure, the film is rewound in the usual way and unloaded from the camera. The exposed film is then loaded into a small desk-top processor together with a cartridge of processing reagents which is supplied with the film. A series of simple operations are then carried out which wind the film into contact with the processing reagents, allow the development to take place and then rewind the dry, processed 35-mm film into its original cassette. After this, which takes a few minutes only, the film may be removed from the cassette and mounted in slide holders. Three types of film are currently available in this range, all intended to produce transparencies for projection. There is a black and white continuous tone film, a high contrast black and white line film (intended for copying diagrams) and a colour film known as 'Polachrome'. This last film is of interest as it is an additive film, with the film base printed with a raster pattern of parallel red, green, and blue lines. A black and white emulsion coated on the **back** of the film is exposed through this raster and is processed to produce a positive transparency in colour. 'Polachrome' is rated nominally at ISO 40 and is balanced for daylight; it is worth noting that if used in a camera system in which metering is by light reflected from the film itself (as in the Olympus, for example) then, because of the low reflectivity of the 'Polachrome' base, it is necessary to adjust the ISO rating set on the camera in order to achieve a correctly-exposed transparency. Experiment with one's own equipment will soon reveal the most acceptable film speed setting. The colour saturation of 'Polachrome' is good and the line structure is not visible in the image when viewed from the screen. With the use of appropriate colour temperature correction filters this film has been found very satisfactory for photomicrography; it reproduces polarization and interference colours particularly well.

6.3. Fluorescence photomicrography

In recent years, there has been a tremendous increase in the use of **fluorescence microscopy**, especially in the biological sciences following the introduction of fluorescent-labelled monoclonal antibodies. Fluorescence microscopy, either with transmitted or reflected light, produces images in which the contrast is very high. The background is dark and the image-forming light originates in the specimen itself as a result of its excitation with radiation of suitable wavelengths. There are several problems in the photomicrography (which is usually carried out in colour) of fluorescent specimens. Among these problems are:

(a)   the generally low level of light emission from the specimen;
(b)   the necessity to ensure that the background records as a true black;
(c)   the tendency of the fluorescence to fade during the exposure; and
(d)   the difficulty of accurate rendering of the fluorescence colours.

Correct microscope technique and photographic practice will, however, usually enable acceptable results to be obtained; it is recommended that accurate records should be kept and, when exposing film, take more shots than are necessary, bracketing the exposures and possibly varying the filter combinations slightly. The problem of low light levels may be alleviated in two ways. First, wherever possible use reflected-light microscopy, as this ensures that there is little or no absorption or quenching of the fluorescence in the thickness of the section. At the same time the objective acts as its own condenser so that there are no problems with centration, focusing or corrections of this optical element. If transmitted-light fluorescence has to be used then it is advisable to use a darkground condenser; this often ensures more concentrated exciting radiation reaching the specimen and (as this radiation is in the form of a hollow cone of numerical aperture *greater* than that of the objective) it also helps ensure that there is a black background to the fluorescent image.

It is good practice to use the lowest possible total magnification that will reveal the necessary detail. Use an objective with the highest possible numerical aperture (NA) as (in transmitted fluorescence) the brightness of the image is proportional to

$$\frac{(\text{Numerical aperture})^2}{(\text{Magnification})^2}$$

With reflected fluorescence the brightness is related to NA^4. From these relationships it is clear that in order to obtain the brightest possible image, the objective NA should be high and its magnification as low as possible. Several manufacturers now market objectives especially designed for fluorescence. These objectives not only have low intrinsic fluorescence, thus avoiding contrast degradation, but also have very high numerical apertures. For example 'dry' 40X objectives with an aperture of 0.85 are commonplace and an oil-immersion 40X objective with a numerical aperture of 1.3 is also available. The second solution to the problem of low-light intensity is to use a high-speed film. At present colour reversal and print films are available with speeds of 100, 200, 400, 600, and even 1000 ISO. If one is prepared to sacrifice some slight print or transparency quality then one of the higher-rated films may be chosen. If still more speed is required, then it should be remembered that almost any colour film now available may be rated at an increased speed. This increase is compensated for by an increased time in the first development, a process known as **push-processing**. Kodak 'Ektachrome' films, for instance, may be given a one-stop increase in speed (with minimal increase in grain and negligible increase in background density) by increasing the first development time by 2 min. By this technique, the 'Ektachrome' daylight films nominally rated at 64,160,200, and 400 ISO have their speeds increased to 125, 320, 400, and 800 ISO, respectively. If the first development time is increased by $5\frac{1}{2}$ min, then these speeds are again doubled, i.e. a two-stop speed increase over the standard values. There may be some increase in grain and loss of density but these may be acceptable if by uprating the film one is able to take fluorescence colour micrographs when otherwise this would not be possible. Many film processing labs provide a push-processing service and if film is developed 'in house', then of course there is no difficulty. For black and white micrographs, it is possible to use either a fast film such as Kodak 'TRI-X' (rated nominally at ISO 400) or an equivalent film from other makers. Because of the varying characteristics of different fluorescence microscopes, of different specimens, and of different developer–film combinations, it is recommended that some practical tests should be carried out with one's own equipment before finalizing the choice of a film-developer combination for this type of work. Even a slow film such as Kodak 'Technical Pan' which has very favourable reciprocity failure characteristics, may be used successfully for fluorescence photomicrography.

If a film with sufficient speed is used, the exposure may often be reduced considerably, which has the advantage of minimizing fading of the fluorescence under the influence of the exciting radiation. It is also worth remembering that there are now several mountant additives (especially *n*-propyl gallate) which are claimed to retard fluorescence fading. These and their use are detailed in the papers by Giloh and Sedat (1982), Johnson and Aravjo (1981), and Valnes and Brandtzaeg (1985) cited in the references. Another simple trick which will help to keep exposures at a minimum is to make sure that all the light is directed to the film plane during the exposure. It is remarkable how much light is diverted from the film by even the simplest viewing prism/monocular head arrangement.

It is also important to ensure that the filter combinations are correct for the fluorochrome in use; even a slight mismatch in the exciter filter combination can cause a significant reduction in the amount of fluorescence, whilst an incorrect barrier filter may appreciably degrade the blackness of the image background.

In colour photomicrography with the fluorescence microscope the representation of the colours is often a matter of personal preference, so that the type of film to be used is a matter of experiment. In all cases with this specialized branch of microscopy, the answer is to try an experimental series of exposures, keeping careful records and basing one's subsequent practice on the results. This empirical approach is also true for the problems of exposure determination, which resemble those found in darkground microscopy. An integrating metering system will almost invariably result in a grossly over-exposed image on the film. If a spot metering system is available, then this will work well if fluorescing material is centred onto the area of the measuring spot. If spot metering is not available, then compensation may be made with the expsoure adjustment control (if it is fitted to the automatic camera), by altering the nominal ISO setting on the camera or by over-riding the automatic exposure mechanism and exposing manually. If in doubt, it is wise to 'bracket' the exposures, spreading the given times by a large amount. Although this may seem wasteful of film, it is easier and cheaper in the long run than the effort of setting up the system again, relocating the correct fields and re-exposing more film, if the first exposures were unusable.

6.4. Prints for publication

For many, the principal purpose of photomicrograph is to obtain suitable pictures to illustrate reports or scientific papers. Often the end results, as submitted to editors, do not justify all the hard effort which has gone into the science. For this reason, a few suggestions as to how prints for publication should be presented may be helpful.

It is worth considering at the early stage of writing a paper or report exactly how many illustrations are necessary in order to clarify the verbal descriptions. In many instances, if the author is truly honest with himself, he would admit that some illustrations are superfluous and the same information could be conveyed in fewer micrographs, perhaps by the judicious use of high-power inserts into irrelevant areas of lower power pictures. Often several illustrations may be combined into one plate, provided that by so doing the final magnification of each is not reduced so much that the relevant detail is lost when the plate is reduced for publication.

Prints for publication should be of the highest possible photographic quality, with an adequate but not excessive range of tonal contrast and with the minimum of extraneous marks due to dust etc. on the negative. It is possible to remove such marks by careful 'spotting' on the print but in scientific illustrations which serve as the record of a piece of research, hand work at this stage is to be avoided if at all possible. When producing the final prints try to ensure clean photographic working, processing the negatives and prints in a dust-free atmosphere, removing dust and drying-marks from the negatives and so on. Prints submitted for publication should be on glossy paper. Some editors ask for them to be unmounted and lightly labelled on the reverse, others ask for the plates to be mounted and labelled by the author. By conforming with the 'instructions to authors' which are published at regular intervals by all scientific journals, the publication date may be accelerated by several months.

Practice varies greatly between journals as to the amount of labelling which they require on the face of the prints. Some wish the author to do this in its entirety, whilst others use their own artists in order to ensure uniformity of style. In the latter case, it is often necessary to provide the relevant information on a tracing-paper overlay attached to the mount card. Any such overlays should be provided with register marks at each corner aligned with the corners of the micrograph in order to help the artist transfer accurately all the required labels. Often labels are added by means of some form of dry transfer lettering, which is available in a variety of sizes and styles. Care should be taken to choose a style which will harmonize with that generally adopted by the journal and make due allowance for possible reduction when choosing the size of the letters. Most labelling is carried out with black lettering. This will cause no problems if the area to be lettered is light in tone, but if this area is dark, or if the letter crosses from light to dark, then it is desirable to improve the visibility of the label by using a white letter or number first and then superimposing, slightly offset to one side, a similar character of the same size and type style but in black. This gives exceptional clarity and is well worth the extra trouble. On any print it should be mandatory to add a magnification bar, indicating 1 μm, 10 μm, or some other suitable size; estimations of size may then be easily made, however much or little the illustration is subsequently altered in size during reproduction.

Certain information written on the back of the picture will materially assist the editor and referees and prevent subsequent mistakes and queries to the author. Among such information one might include:

- Name of author(s)
- Title of paper
- Number of micrograph or plate
- Orientation of micrograph.

In some cases the orientation may be immaterial, but if it is desirable to print the micrograph in a given orientation then this should be indicated by the word 'top', with an indicating arrow. Note that all such markings on the reverse of a print should be carried out **lightly**, with a soft B or BB pencil. Care must be taken not to 'dig in' and thus mark the surface of a glossy print.

If the prints are to be mounted then this should be carried out onto suitable white card either by using a standard dry-mounting technique or by one of the more modern 'cold-mount' techniques, which allow easy positioning (and re-positioning) of the print for alignment. This type of mounting is very good for use with colour prints; as no heat is involved (unlike conventional dry mounting) there is no risk of damaging the sensitive colour emulsion of a print.

In conclusion, it is worth perhaps stressing that after all the time and trouble which have been expended to take, process, mount, and label a set of micrographs it is well worth making sure that they reach the editor of the journal in good condition. This means providing sufficient packing all round the pictures to make absolutely sure that they will not be creased or folded during their passage through the postal system.

References

Angel, H. (1983). *The book of close-up photography*. Ebury Press, London.

Arnold, C.R., Rolls, P.J. and Stewart, J.C.J. (1971). *Applied photography*. Focal Press, London.

Blaker, A.A. (1977). *Handbook for scientific photography*. W.H. Freeman & Co., San Francisco.

Bracegirdle, B. (1983). An outline of technique for photomacrography. *Proc. Roy. micr. Soc.*, **18**, 105–17.

Bradbury, S. (1984). *An introduction to the optical microscope*. RMS Handbook No. 01, Royal Microscopical Society/Oxford University Press, Oxford.

—— (1985). Filters in microscopy. *Proc. Roy. micr. Soc.*, **20**, 83–91.

Brandeis, A. (1984). *Colour printing and processing*. Blandford Press, Poole, Dorset.

Brück, A. (1984). *Close-up photography in practice*. David & Charles, Newton Abbot, Devon.

Croy, O.R. (1961). *Camera close up*. Focal Press, London.

Freeman, M. (1983). *Photographic trouble shooter*. MacDonald, London.

Giloh, H. and Sedat, J.W. (1982). Fluorescence microscopy: reduced photobleaching of rhodamine and fluorescein protein conjugates by *n*-propyl gallate. *Science*, **217**, 1252–5.

Hayman, R. (1984). *Filters*. Focal Press, London.

Jacobson, R.E. (1978). *Manual of photography* (formerly the *Ilford Manual of Photography*), 7th edn, Focal Press, London.

Jenny, L. and Panozzo-Heilbronner, R. (1981a). Problems in practical macrography and incient-light micrography. Part 1. Light sources and their spectral characteristics. *Mikroskopion*, No. 37, 4–11.

——, —— (1981b). Problems in practical macrography and incident-light micrography Part 2. Arrangement and presentation of the subject. *Mikroskopion*, No. 38, 4–12.

Johnson, G.D. and Araujo, G.M. de C.N. (1981). A simple method of reducing the fading of immunofluorescence during microscopy. *J. Immunological Methods*, **43**, 349–50.

Kodak Publications (1981). *Contrast index – a criterion for development*, Pamphlet F14.

—— (1977). *Applied infra-red photography*, Publication M28.

—— (1983). *Biomedical imaging information. Tips for succesful fluorescence photomicrography*, EAM-1.

—— (1980). *Photography through the microscope*, P2.

Langford, M.J. (1969). *Advanced photography*. Focal Press, London.

—— (1971). *Basic photography*, 2nd edn, Focal Press, London.

Lawrence, M.J. (1980). The use of fibre optics in video-micrography in BBC Open University Productions. *Proc. Roy. micr. Soc.*, **15**, 425–30.

Lefkowitz, L. (1979). *The Manual of close-up photography*. Amphoto, New York.

Loveland, R.P. (1970). *Photomicrography – a comprehensive treatise*. Vols 1 & 2, J. Wiley, New York.

Reynolds, L.C. (1984). *Lenses*. Focal Press, London.

Shillaber, C.P. (1944). *Photomicrography in theory and practice*. J. Wiley, New York.

Stroebel, L., Compton, J., Current, I., and Zakia, R. (1986). *Photographic materials and processes*. Focal Press, Boston.

Valnes, K. and Brandtzaeg, P. (1985). Retardation of immunofluorescence fading during microscopy. *J. Hist. Cytochemistry, 33*, 755–61.

Wakefield, G. (1982). *Colour films*. Focal press, London.

Walker, M.I. (1971). *Amateur photomicrography*. Focal Press, London.

Index

Plate 1. (A) The objects illustrated in Figure 6, photographed in their natural colours.

(B) The colour wheel; note that complementary colours lie diametrically opposite to each other on the wheel.

Plate 2. A colour transparency of a slide of kidney, stained with the AZAN trichrome technique. Magnification c. × 450. The colour film was balanced for light at a colour temperature of c. 5500 K.

(A) Photographed with the light at the correct temperature of 5500 K; the rendering of the colours in this transparency closely approximates to their appearance in the section.

(B) Photographed with the colour temperature of the illumination reduced to 3250 K. Note the pronounced reddish colour in which many of the stained components in the section now appear.

ERRATUM

Plate 2 (*inside back cover*):
Labels A and B should be
transposed.